LIQUEFIED GASES
Marine Transportation and Storage

Alain Vaudolon

WITHERBY Seamanship
INTERNATIONAL

Witherby Seamanship International
A Division of Witherby Publishing Group Ltd
4 Dunlop Square, Livingston, Edinburgh, EH54 8SB, Scotland, UK
Tel No: +44(0)1506 463 227 - Fax No: +44(0)1506 468 999
Email: info@emailws.com - Web: www.witherbyseamanship.com

First Published 2000
Reprinted 2010

ISBN 1 85609 197 8

British Library Cataloguing in Publication Data
A catalogue record for this book is available from the British Library.

Printed and bound in Great Britain by Bell & Bain Ltd, Glasgow

Published by

Witherby Publishing Group Ltd
4 Dunlop Square, Livingston,
Edinburgh, EH54 8SB,
Scotland, UK

Tel No: +44(0)1506 463 227
Fax No: +44(0)1506 468 999

Email: info@emailws.com
Web: www.witherbys.com

ACKNOWLEDGEMENTS

This book would not have been written without the help of the many friends and colleagues with whom I had the honour and pleasure to work during all those years spent running after liquefied gas tankers. I am grateful to Mr Claude Detourne, Senior Vice-President, Gaz de France and President, International Gas Union, for putting his name to the Foreword. I extend special thanks to Chris Clucas, Consultant, Dorchester Marine, who took the trouble to read the complete draft and suggest many valuable improvements; Richard Eddy, Consultant, Osprey Maritime and Jean Marie Poitou, Consultant, Gas-Team who did the same with various sections and Roger Roue, Technical Adviser, SIGTTO, who let me choose photographs from the large library he is setting up. Dave Cullen, Vice President, Ebara Cryodynamics, Andre Raymond, Sales Director, Foxboro, Jacques Delhemes, President, Gaz Transport & Technigaz, Yoshitoh Okumura, General Manager, Ishikawajima Harima Heavy Industries, Yoshiaki Tamura, General Manager, The Kansai Electric Corporation, Alain Dorange, Managing Director, KSB-AMRI, Captain Shahib Sabeh, Marine Superintendent, Malaysia LNG, all provided photographs of the products they represent. A special mention of my late and sadly missed friend Captain Jean Trevedy who provided some of the stories in Chapter 12. I must certainly not omit the help received from my daughter Sophie in solving some tricky computer graphic problems and from my wife Theresa who was brave enough to read the full draft and correct my occasional franglais and numerous spelling errors.

Alain Vaudolon
July 2000

FOREWORD

by Monsieur Claude Detourne

Inspecteur General Du Gaz De France President – International Gas Union

The known world reserves of gas are larger than those of oil and yet, for a long time, this gas did not attract much interest. On the contrary, it was considered a hindrance by those involved in the recovery of oil. For many years, the associated gas was flared and the dry wells containing natural gas were ignored.

At the beginning of the century, when the first attemps at industrial production of gas were made, it was recognised that gas had the potential to change the world's way of living. LPG, by providing bottled gas, has transformed the way millions of people heat their homes and cook. Development of chemical gases has brought tremendous changes to people's lives by providing them with all sorts of cheap plastic objects, tyres for their cars, fertilisers for growing their crops. The development of natural gas has made available a clean source of energy, replacing old town gas, and providing a competitive and clean alternative for industrial use and the production of electricity.

Gas, however, like oil and coal, needs to be transported from the production sites, usually located in sparsely populated areas, to where it is needed. The transportation of oil and coal was straightforward and could be very quickly developed on a large scale. The transportation of gas, however, presented a number of technological problems which demanded a little more attention.

Gas can be used at the point of production, but there is not usually much demand. In recent years, large refineries, producing valuable chemicals, have been developed in gas-producing countries, but this only uses a fraction of the available quantity.

Gas can be transported in two ways. In gaseous form, under high pressure through large pipelines, or in liquefied form, by ship. The pipeline option is extensively used but it is only viable under certain conditions; parameters such as the quantity to be transported, the distance over which it has to be transported, the depth of water to be crossed and the amount of required initial investment limit its application. Transportation by ship is usually flexible enough to accommodate the fluctuations of the market, reliable enough to satisfy long-term users and economical enough for the gas to compete successfully against other products.

The opportunity was there to create and develop a new industry, derived from traditional shipping but with very specific requirements. It involved not only the ships at sea but also the production and storage units ashore. As soon as the means became available, the growth of the transport of petroleum and chemical gases was quite spectacular and yet, this was nothing compared to what has happened with the development of LNG.

This book reviews the history of the marine transportation of liquefied gases and the conditions which are prevailing today. It was not intended to go into explicit technical detail but to try to give an overview of all the aspects of the industry, covering the characteristics of the ships, the rules and regulations in force, details of storage tanks on shore and a look at safety and reliability. It should provide valuable general information to all those who are involved in the marine transportation of liquefied gases, including ship and terminal operators, ships agents, port authorities, charterers, cargo traders, insurance brokers and underwriters.

The book reflects the author's accumulated experience during his distinguished career in gas shipping.

1. *Mast to be Installed in a Gaz Transport Membrane Type Tank.*

CONTENTS

THE AUTHOR

 Alain Vaudolon has been closely involved with the gas shipping industry since 1969. He started his sea-going career as an engineer cadet in 1959, finishing as chief engineer on a semi-pressurised LPG carrier at the end of the 1960's. Prior to that, he spent time as replacement Chief Engineer sailing on 9 different ships in two and a half years. Since then he has held technical and operational posts in LPG and LNG carrier fleets in various parts of the world including France, the U.K, the United States, Malaysia and Japan. He has been closely associated with two Malaysian LNG shipping projects, first with Malaysian International Shipping Corporation as LNG Technical Manager, later LNG Manager Fleet Operation and then with Petronas Tankers Sdn. Bhd. as LNG Shipping Project Manager. In both cases, he was closely involved in the design, construction supervision, acceptance of delivery and organisation of the operation of two series of five, French built, LNG tankers.

A particularly interesting and satisfying aspect of his time with MISC was the introduction of a training scheme, sending groups of young Malaysians to navigation schools in the U.K. with the objective being to fully Malaysianise the crews of the LNG carriers. Some 10 years on, with few exceptions, the full complement of the five ships was Malaysian. At the initiation of the second LNG project by Petronas Tankers, quite a few of the first group of cadets were actively participating in supervisory positions.

In July 1995 Alain Vaudolon was appointed General Manager of the Society of International Gas Tanker and Terminal Operators (SIGTTO) and he remained in this position until January 1999. This was another very challenging period, during which he was also closely involved with the deliberations at the International Maritime Organization.

REFERENCES

1. *International Convention for the Safety Of Life At Sea (SOLAS)* Latest 1998 edition – International Maritime Organization (IMO)

2. *International Convention for the Prevention of Pollution from Ships* (MARPOL) 73/78 – Latest edition 1998 – (IMO)

3. *International Code for the Construction and Equipment of Ships Carrying Liquefied Gases in Bulk* (IGC Code) – 1993 – (IMO)

4. *International Convention on Standard of Training, Certification and Watchkeeping for Seafarers* 1978 as amended by the 1995 Convention (IMO)

5. *Recommendations on the Safe Transport, Handling and Storage of Dangerous Substances in Port* –1983, revised 1995 – (IMO)

6. *APELL for Port Areas 1996 – Awareness and Preparedness for Emergencies at Local Level – IMO/UNEP* – (IMO)

7. *COMAH – Control of Major Accident Hazards Regulations* – European Directive 96/82/EC

8. *A Guide for the Control of Industrial Major Accident Hazards Regulation 1984* – Health and Safety Executive, HMSO

9. *Liquefied Gas Handling Principles on Ships and in Terminals* – Third Edition 2000 – (SIGTTO)

10. *Guidelines for Hazard Analysis as an Aid to Management of Safe Operations* – 1992 (SIGTTO)

11. *Training of Terminal Staff Involved in Loading and Discharging Gas Carriers* – 1996 (SIGTTO)

12. *A Guide to Contingency Planning for the Gas Carrier at Sea and in Port Approaches* – 2000 – (ICS/OCIMF/SIGTTO)

13. *A Guide to Contingency Planning for the Gas Carrier Alongside and Within Port Limits* – 1999 – (ICS/OCIMF/SIGTTO)

14. *A Guide to Contingency Planning for Marine Terminals Handling Liquefied Gases in Bulk* – 1999 – (ICS/OCIMF/SIGTTO)

15. *Ship to Ship Transfer Guide (Liquefied Gases)* – 1995 – (ICS/OCIMF/SIGTTO)

16. *Tanker Safety Guide – Liquefied Gases (Including the International Safety Check List for Gas Carriers)* – 1995 – (ICS)

17. *Dangerous Goods in Ports: Recommendations for Port Designs and Port Operators* – 1985 – (Permanent International Association of Navigation Congresses – PIANC)

18. *Refinery Safety Guide* – Institute of Petroleum

19. *Guide on Marine Terminal Fire Protection and Emergency Evacuation* – 1987 – OCIMF

20. *Natural Gas by Sea – The Development of a New Technology* – 1993 – Roger Ffooks

21. *Gas Pioneers* – Roland Hautefeuille, Richard Clayton – Fairplay International

LIST OF ILLUSTRATIONS

2. Cargo Manifold Platform on a LNG Tanker.

CHARTS AND DRAWINGS

3. *Semi Pressurised LPG Tanker in the North Pacific.*

DEFINITIONS

APELL Awareness and Preparedness for Emergencies at Local Level. A ten-step process instituted by the United Nations Environment Program (UNEP) to help decision makers and technical personnel improve or create community awareness of hazardous installations and integrated joint emergency plans.

Accuracy Deviation of the average value of measurements from the true value.

Aerating Introduction of fresh air into a space with the object of removing toxic and inert gas to make the atmosphere suitable for entry by personnel.

Alarm Signal given by a control system when a parameter is beyond set limits or by an operator when an abnormal situation is developing.

Ambient The medium or space surrounding a body.

BLEVE Boiling Liquid Expanding Vapour Explosion. Associated with the rupture under fire conditions of a pressure vessel containing liquid gas.

BWM Ballast Water Management.

Ballast Any solid or liquid mass placed on a ship to increase the draught, change the trim or regulate stability.

Boiling Point The temperature at which the vapour pressure of a liquid equals that of the pressure at its surface.

Boil-off Liquid vaporisation due to heat transfer into cargo transported near its boiling point. If a perfect insulation was available, there would be no boil-off.

Booster pump A pump used to increase the discharge pressure from another pump.

Brittle fracture Fracture of a material caused by lack of ductility, usually with very little plastic deformation. One possible cause of brittle fracture can be exposure of the material to low temperatures.

Bulk An homogeneous cargo carried in tanks or pressure vessels which are constructed as part of the ship and which is loaded and discharged by the ship's installed handling system is carried "in bulk".

Bulkhead Vertical partition which subdivides the interior of a ship into separate compartments.

Calibration The act of checking and ascertaining graduation of scales with measuring instruments or by physical trials; checking the performance of equipment against known or designed values.

Calorific value The quantity of heat released per unit of weight of a fuel.

Capacitance gauge When the liquid level changes, the capacitance of a long coaxial sensor installed in the tank from its bottom to its top changes. Measuring the variation of capacitance indicates the position of the liquid level.

Capital element It is the part of the charter hire which provides funds for the owner's return on his investment in the vessel.

Carbon Dioxide   A neutral gas which is present in the products of fuel combustion - Chemical formula CO_2. Also used as a refrigerant gas and for fire-fighting, particularly electric fires.

Carbon Monoxide   Highly toxic substance produced by incomplete combustion of carbon based materials, in particular hydrocarbons. Chemical formula CO.

Carcinogen   A substance capable of causing cancer.

Cargo   Merchandise conveyed on a ship.

Cargo containment   The arrangement of containment for cargo on a gas tanker including, where fitted, a primary and secondary barrier, associated insulation and any intervening spaces and adjacent structure, if necessary for the support of these elements.

Cargo manifold   The piping, valves and flanges through which bulk liquid carriers receive and discharge their cargo. Usually situated at midship.

Cargo operations   Any operations on board a gas carrier involving the handling of cargo liquid or vapour, e.g. cargo transfer, reliquefaction, inerting etc.

Certificate of Fitness   A certificate issued by or on behalf of the Flag Administration confirming that the structure, equipment, fittings, arrangements and materials used in the construction of a gas carrier are in compliance with the relevant IMO Gas Codes. Such certification may be issued on behalf of the Administration by approved Classification Societies.

Charter party   A contract whereby a shipowner agrees to place his ship, or part of it, at the disposal of a trader or other person (known as the charterer) for the carriage of goods from one port to another, for which he is paid freight; or to let

his ship for a specified period, his renumeration being known as hire money.

Chemical tanker   Vessels specially designed to carry chemicals, many of which are highly poisonous, corrosive or volatile. Built according to the IMO BCH Code.

Classification Societies   Non profit-making organisations directed by committees representing shipowners, shipbuilders, engine-builders and underwriters, for the purpose of ensuring that ships are constructed as per the current rules and maintained in seaworthy condition. They make rules governing ship construction, arrange and carry out surveys during the building of a ship and throughout the vessel's trading life and can be empowered by Flag States to ensure ship's compliance with national regulations.

Cofferdam   A space between bulkheads or decks to prevent leakage between adjoining compartments.

Compressor   Machinery used to increase the pressure of a gas. Compressors may be reciprocating, centrifugal or rotary.

Critical pressure   The pressure at which a substance exists in a liquid state at its critical temperature. It can also be described as the saturation pressure at the critical temperature.

Critical temperature   The temperature above which a gas cannot exist as a liquid.

Cryogenics   The study of the behaviour of matter at very low temperature.

Custody transfer   The process by which ownership or custody of a cargo is transferred between contracting parties, usually before loading or discharging. This includes the measurement of volume, temperature and composition.

Deadweight   The maximum weight of cargo, bunkers, stores etc. that a vessel can carry whilst floating with a specific freeboard, (e.g. summer deadweight is the maximum a vessel can load whilst floating at summer draught in salt water).

Deepwell pump A type of centrifugal cargo pump commonly found on gas carriers. The prime mover is usually an electric or hydraulic motor mounted on the top of the cargo tank dome and driving, through a double seal arrangement, the pump assembly located at the bottom of the tank.

Demurrage An agreed daily amount, specified in the charter party, which is to be paid by the charterer, in case of delays to the ship that are not caused by the ship, that result in Laytime being exceeded.

Density The mass-per-unit volume of a substance at specified conditions of temperature and pressure.

Dew point The temperature at which a sample of air is saturated with the amount of water vapour it contains. Any further reduction in temperature creates condensation.

Drip tray Container located under flanges, valves or a tank to collect the eventual dripping resulting from a leak. A drip tray may be fixed or portable.

Dry-break coupling Device fitted in a hard-arm and installed between two valves to provide a means of quick disconnection with a very small amount of cargo spillage in case of an emergency. The action of the dry-break coupling is usually hydraulically controlled and is linked with the actuation of the two valves.

Dry chemical powder The main dry chemical powders used to extinguish small LNG and LPG fires are sodium bicarbonate, potassium bicarbonate and urea potassium bicarbonate. The powder is contained in a pressure-resistant container and propelled, when necessary, by compressed gas, such as nitrogen. Dry chemical powder is also suitable for extinguishing electrical fires.

Emergency Shut-Down System Emergency Shut-Down system (ESD) applies to the ship to shore interface. It is designed to protect ship and shore in the event of dangerous conditions developing during cargo transfer. The system employs valves which close at the ship's manifold and also isolate the shore facilities in a sequential fashion, minimising the risks of surge. The ship's cargo pumps and shore pumps are stopped during the process. Initiation can be by hand, both from the ship and from the shore, or automatic when sensing equipment registers abnormal conditions such as gas detection or tank overfill.

F.O.B. Cargo delivery term – Free On Board – The responsibility for meeting all charges for damage or loss of cargo passes from the seller or exporter to the importer or buyer when the cargo crosses the ship's rail onto the vessel.

Fender Resilient device, usually movable, interposed between a ship's hull and harbour walls or other ships to minimise impact and prevent direct contact, thus reducing risk of structural damage or chafing. Often of rubber compound, timber or pneumatic construction.

Fibre-optic Glass or plastic fibre wire allowing the transmission of light signals, even over very long distances.

Flag State The government of the country in which the ship is registered. This is the authority that issues some of the certificates related to the operation of a ship, and is responsible for inspections to ensure compliance with appropriate national and international standards.

Flammable Capable of being ignited and burning in air.

Flare An isolated chimney or pipe fitted with a pilot flame, at the end of which unusable gases are burned.

Float gauge Device installed in a tank to measure the level by means of a float on top of the liquid surface which drives a tape allowing the liquid level to be read outside the tank.

Foundering When a ship fills with water and sinks.

Free surface The effect on a ship's stability of unrestrained redistribution of liquid as a vessel heels to either side with tanks partially filled.

Gas analyser An instrument able to indicate the amount of a certain type of gas present in the atmosphere being tested.

Gas carrier A tanker designed to carry liquefied petroleum gases, either pressurised at ambient temperature or fully refrigerated at a pressure slightly above atmospheric pressure, or semi-pressurised at a pressure between 5 and 7 bar.

Gassing-up The operation of replacing an inert atmosphere in a tank with a suitable amount of vapour from the next cargo, to allow cooling down and loading.

Gas Carrier Codes The Gas Carrier Codes are the codes for the construction and equipment of ships carrying liquefied gases in bulk. These standards are set and published by IMO. They are the Gas Carrier Code, the Gas Carrier Code for Existing Ships and the International Gas Carrier Code.

Gas-freeing The process of removing toxic or flammable vapours from a tank, compartment or container, followed by the introduction of fresh air into the tank, compartment or container.

HAZOP Hazard and Operability study - Hazard identification technique, which considers the effects of deviation from the normal operating intent by identifying basic causes, their immediate effects and the resultant consequences.

Hold space The space enclosed by the ship's structure in which a cargo containment system is situated.

Hydrates The compounds, in the form of crystalline substances, formed by the interaction of water and hydrocarbons at certain pressures and temperatures.

Hydrocarbon An organic compound formed from hydrogenated carbon. Natural gases are primarily composed of hydrocarbons. Crude oil is a mixture of hydrocarbons.

IMO International Maritime Organization - A specialised agency of the United Nations; its role is to facilitate co-operation between governments on technical matters affecting international shipping, such as navigation, safety, dangerous cargo shipment code and pollution control. Prior to 1982, known as IMCO.

IBC Code International Code for the Construction and Equipment of Ships Carrying Dangerous Chemicals in Bulk.

Inert gas A single gas, such as nitrogen, or a mixture of gases containing insufficient oxygen to support combustion.

Inerting Inerting means:

(1) The introduction of inert gas into an aerated tank in order to reduce the oxygen content to a level at which combustion cannot be supported or to obtain an inert condition suited to a safe gassing-up operation.

(2) The introduction of inert gas into a tank after cargo discharge and warming-up with the aim of:

(a) Reducing flammable vapour content to a level below which combustion cannot be supported if aeration takes place.

(b) Reducing existing vapour content to a level suited to gassing-up prior to a new cargo.

(c) Reducing existing oxygen or cargo vapour content to a level stipulated by local authorities when a special gas-free certificate for hot work is required.

Insulation Any form of barrier restricting the flow of heat or electric current from one body to another is said to insulate them and the non-conducting material used is called insulation.

Invar A metal composed of about 60% iron and 40% nickel which has a negligible coefficient of thermal expansion. It is used in the fabrication of the Gaz Transport membrane system of containment for LNG and also for measuring tapes and clock balance wheels.

Jettison Voluntary act of throwing or pumping overboard cargo, stores etc., when a ship is at risk.

Jetty A pier, mole or breakwater running out into the sea. It may be used as a landing pier.

LFL Lower Flammable Limit – The concentration of a hydrocarbon gas in air below which there is insufficient hydrocarbon to support combustion.

LNG Liquefied Natural Gas – In liquid form, natural gas occupies 600 times less volume than in gas form, which makes possible its transport by container. The temperature of LNG at atmospheric pressure is approximately $-160°C$, depending on its composition.

LPG Liquefied Petroleum Gas – LPG can be obtained during the production of gasoline. It is undesirable in petrol engines because of its high volatility. LPG can also be produced from Natural Gas or associated gases. The heavier gases, propane C_3H_8 and butane C_4H_{10}, are separated, compressed until liquid and stored under pressure in steel cylinders for industrial and domestic use. At atmospheric pressure, propane boils at $-42.2°C$ and butane at $-0.5°C$.

Laid up A ship that has been decommissioned, normally with reduced manning, due to the market or other conditions being unsuitable for its continued operation.

Liquefied gas A liquid which has a saturated vapour pressure exceeding 2.8 bar absolute at 37.8°C formed by refrigeration, pressurisation or a combination of both and certain other substances of similar characteristics specified in the IMO Gas Codes.

Loading arm An articulated metal arm used at terminal jetties to connect shore pipelines to the ship's manifold.

MARPOL The International Convention for the Prevention of Pollution from Ships, 1973/78, consolidated 1991 with late amendments (up to 1997).

Melting plug A mechanical device which melts at a prescribed temperature, precipitating a safety shut-down of the system it protects.

Membrane tank A container for LNG comprising a thin metallic liquid-tight lining, completely supported by load-bearing insulation. This, in turn, is supported by the structure of the ship.

Methane A hydrocarbon gas, the simplest of the paraffins. Methane (CH_4) is used as an industrial and domestic fuel.

Mooring A means of attaching a floating vessel to a fixed structure by using a system of mooring lines.

Mounded Describes a horizontal cylindrical tank covered with a layer of earth.

Nox Abbreviation for Oxides of Nitrogen which are present during fuel combustion. They are considered to be pollutants and a prime cause of acid rain.

Natural gas Underground accumulation of gas of widely varying composition which may or may not be associated with deposits of oil. Most oil accumulations have natural gas dissolved in the oil and often a "gas cap" of free gas above the oil.

Nitrogen Gaseous element which forms about four-fifths of the earth's atmosphere. It is an inert gas.

Non-destructive Testing Processes for testing for properties, quality or soundness of materials or components, which can be applied without causing damage. Typical non-destructive test processes include radiography, dye penetrant, magnetic particle and ultrasonic methods for detecting internal flaws or cracks.

Non-return valve A valve in a pipeline which will automatically close if the direction of fluid flow is reversed.

OCIMF Oil Companies International Marine Forum

Oxygen Gaseous element which forms about one fifth of the earth's atmosphere. Oxygen (O_2) is a reactive gas which supports combustion.

PERC Powered Emergency Release Coupling, fitted to hard-arms to allow quick disconnection of the arm in case of emergency.

Parts per million (ppm) The measure of a concentration of a substance when mixed with another as millionth parts of the whole.

Perlite A natural mineral insulation material produced by heat treatment of volcanic stones. Used in both LPG and LNG containment systems.

Pilot A locally licensed navigator who advises the master in local waters on manoeuvring the passage to and from the berth.

Polymerisation The phenomenon by which the molecules of a particular compound link together into a. larger unit containing anything from two to thousands of molecules. The new unit is called a polymer.

Port Authority The Authority (person or body) empowered to exercise effective control in a port area, who is responsible for port services and facilities.

Port State The government of the country in which a port is situated. Not related to Flag State.

Port State Control The Paris Memorandum of Understanding on Port State Control is a regional administrative agreement, concluded in Paris on 26 January 1982 by the maritime authorities of 14 European countries. In this memorandum of understanding, the participating maritime authorities agree to establish, in their ports, a harmonised system of Port State Control, with the aim of eliminating the operation of sub-standard ships.

Other memoranda of Understanding on Port States Control cover South & Latin America (Viña del Mar), Far East (Tokyo), Caribbean & Central America (Caribbean), North Africa & Levant (Mediterranean), Gulf, Mauritius, India (Indian Ocean). West & Central Africa is in preparation.

Primary barrier The innermost surface of a cargo containment system which is normally in contact with the cargo.

QC/DC Quick Connect/Disconnect Coupling – A means of connecting the hose or arm to the vessels cargo manifold without the requirement for bolts. It may be hydraulically or manually operated.

Regulatory Authority The national, provincial or local authority empowered to lay down and enforce legally binding requirements in respect of port areas.

Relief valve Valve loaded by spring or other means to release fluid from a system when the pressure in the system matches a preset level.

Reliquefaction Converting cargo boil-off vapour back into a liquid by refrigeration.

Return gas blower A blower used to return gas from the ship to shore or shore to ship during cargo transfer operations.

Risk analysis The process of analysing a particular business or investment situation with a view to determining the risk areas and how they can best be minimised.

Roll over The situation where the stability of two, inverted, stratified layers of liquid of differing relative densities is disturbed, resulting in a spontaneous rapid mixing of the layers, accompanied, in the case of liquefied gases, by a violent vapour evolution.

SIGTTO The Society of International Gas Tanker and Terminal Operators.

SOLAS Safety of Life at Sea – The International Convention for the Safety of Life at Sea (SOLAS) 1960 and 1974, consolidated 1997, adopted by the International Maritime Organization (IMO). The most important of all international treaties concerning the safety of merchant ships, also

one of the oldest. There have been a number of amendments since 1980.

STCW Convention International Convention on Standards of Training, Certification and Watchkeeping for Seafarers, 1978, as amended in 1995.

Safety check list A list of safety-related items that are checked prior to starting and during an operation.

Safety valve A valve which opens automatically in the event of excess pressure in a container.

Saturated Vapour Pressure The pressure exerted by a boiling liquid vapour at a given temperature within a container.

Secondary barrier The liquid resistant outer element of a cargo containment system, designed to afford temporary containment of leakage of liquid cargo through the primary barrier.

Ship survey Examination of ship's hull and machinery by surveyor of shipowner's classification society organisation.

Soot Black deposit resulting from the combustion of hydrocarbon products.

Specific gravity The ratio of the density of a liquid at a given temperature to the density of fresh water at a standard temperature.

Spray pump A small pump used to send product under pressure through the spray lines within a cargo tank for the purpose of cooling the tank and the contained vapour.

Stripping pump A pump used to discharge the residual cargo which the main cargo pumps cannot lift.

Submerged pump A type of centrifugal pump commonly installed on gas carriers and at terminals in the bottom of a cargo tank. It comprises drive motor, impeller and bearings totally submerged by the cargo when the tank contains bulk liquid of dielectric characteristics. If the cargo conducts electricity, the electric motor has to be enclosed and made tight.

Surge pressure   A phenomenon generated in a pipeline system when there is a change in the rate of flow of liquid in the line. Surge pressure can be dangerously high if the change of flow rate is too rapid and the resultant shock waves can damage pumping equipment and cause rupture of pipelines and associated equipment.

Time charter   The hiring of a vessel for a specific period or number of voyages. The owner pays for insurance of the ship, wages, stores, etc. The charterer must pay for bunker fuel, fresh water, stevedoring, port charges, pilotage etc.

Trim   Difference between forward and aft draught of a ship.

UFL   Upper Flammable Limit – The concentration of a hydrocarbon gas in air above which there is insufficient air to support combustion

Vapour   Gaseous form of a normally liquid or solid substance

Vapour barrier   Thin watertight lining placed on top of insulation to prevent the ingress of water vapour.

Vaporiser   A heat exchanger used to vaporise liquid gasses.

Void space   An enclosed space in the cargo area or other part of a ship, not being a hold space, ballast space, fuel oil tank, cargo pump or compressor room, or any space in normal use by personnel.

Water-spray system   A system to provide a blanket of water droplets to cover the cargo manifolds, tank domes, deck storage tanks and boundaries of superstructure and deckhouses.

4. *Inside a Membrane Tank of the Gaz Transport Type.*

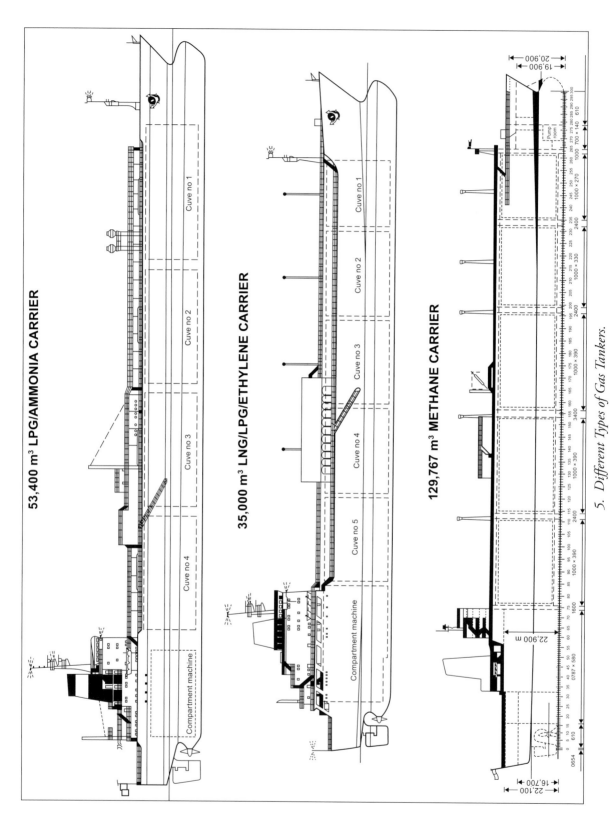

53,400 m³ LPG/AMMONIA CARRIER

Cuve no 1

Cuve no 2

Cuve no 3

Cuve no 4

Compartment machine

35,000 m³ LNG/LPG/ETHYLENE CARRIER

Cuve no 1

Cuve no 2

Cuve no 3

Cuve no 4

Cuve no 5

Compartment machine

129,767 m³ METHANE CARRIER

Pump room

5. *Different Types of Gas Tankers.*

Chapter 1
INTRODUCTION

The marine transportation of liquefied gases is a very small part of the shipping industry. With slightly more than 1,000 ships over one thousand cubic meter capacity, it does not stand comparison to the 3,000 chemical tankers, the 7,000 oil tankers and the 44,000 other types of ships of similar sizes. And yet, for many different reasons, it is a very important part of the shipping world. Compared to the rest of shipping, which is as old as the oldest civilisation, the marine transportation of liquefied gases is very new. It is just over 60 years since the first attempt was made to transport LPG in bulk and it is but 40 years since "Methane Pioneer" carried the first cargo of LNG. LPG and LNG are among the least polluting of the energy sources known in the world today. The accidental release of a gas tanker's cargo might result in a serious fire but little, if any, lasting environmental pollution. The safety record of the liquefied gas fleet is second to none and gas tankers are listed by all Port State Controls as the type of ship showing the least number of discrepancies. Paradoxically, liquefied gas ships have been described, in a certain type of alarmist literature, as being the potential cause of large catastrophic accidents. One famous book, published at the end of the 1970's, described in great detail how the whole of New York City would be reduced to ashes following the explosion of an LNG tanker, waiting to discharge at a terminal there. Good scaremongering fiction! But to anyone not directly involved in this branch of the shipping industry, the marine transportation of liquefied gases can seem mysterious and remote.

This book is a very modest attempt at giving interested parties a brief description of some aspects of the marine transportation of liquefied gases. What are the products covered by the term liquefied gases, what sort of ships are used for their carriage, how are these ships loaded and discharged, how are the products stored on shore before being loaded on the ships, these are questions which, hopefully, should appear slightly clearer to whoever is brave enough or interested enough to read this book.

My interest in gas tankers started when I was dispatched to Tokyo, Japan, at the end of 1968, to relieve the Chief Engineer of a 12,000 cubic meter semi-pressurised LPG carrier, trading butadiene between Nagasaki, Japan and New Orleans, USA. It was an interesting adventure with many "firsts", not least my first of many visits to Japan but, more to the point, my first contact with a gas tanker. It was fortunate that the next sea passage lasted 35 days and that my Chief Engineer colleague, to his great disappointment, was asked to stay on board to show me some of the intricacies of the ship's cargo equipment, which, in those early years, was the Chief Engineer's responsibility. It was not without some trepidation that I saw him jump ashore as soon as the ship was alongside in New Orleans, leaving me to discharge the cargo and inert the tanks in preparation for the next loading. Following this interesting start, the next 30 years were given over to the ships used for the marine transportation of liquefied gases. I had the chance of building, operating, modifying, salvaging and repairing many of them, from the smallest pressurised LPG carrier to the largest LNG tanker.

The development of the marine transportation of liquefied gases has been quite spectacular. After the first attempts at bulk carriage of LPG before World War II and a relatively small development in pressurised transport after the war, it was the possibility of transporting LPG and chemical gases in refrigerated condition at atmospheric pressure at the end of the 1950's that marked the start of the real development of the trade. From slightly more than 100 ships of a few thousand cubic meters capacity at the end of the 1950's, the number and the size of ships in the fleet increased rapidly. The first "large" (28,875 m³) refrigerated ship was completed and delivered in Japan in 1962 and its European equivalent appeared two years after. The beginning of the 1970's saw ships of 50,000 m³ capacity with 70,000, 80,000 and 100,000 m³ following close behind. The number of ships over 1,000 m³ capacity was 200 at the end of the 1960's, 400 at the end of the 1970's and now exceeds 900, with the total capacity of the fleet standing at over 11 million cubic meters and the number of loaded voyages per year probably above 18,000.

The development of the LNG fleet has been even more spectacular. The first ships came into service in 1964, with capacities of 27,400 m³. The fleet progressed from 9 ships at the end of the 1960's to 49 ships at the end of the 70's, 71 ships at the end of the 1980's and 117 ships at the end of January 2000. Correspondingly, the total fleet capacity went from 383,000 m³ to 4.3 Mm³, 7.0 Mm³ and 12.5 Mm³ and the total number of loaded voyages completed is, today, probably more than 28,000. In 1998, close to 2,000 loaded voyages were completed with a total of more than 82 million tonnes transported.

The progression of the LNG trade has not always been smooth. In 1983, 27 LNG tankers were laid up in various parts of the world for economical and commercial reasons and some of them stayed that way for many years. Some of these ships have not transported one single cargo of LNG to this day and some were scrapped after only one or two years' service. One well known chronicler of the LNG shipping industry had this comment to make at the time: "to be the owner of LNG tonnage, you need to have the patience of Job, the deep pockets of Croesus and the longevity of Methuselah". However, in the whole history of LNG transport, there have been only two years, 1980 and 1981, during which the number of loaded voyages were less than the year before.

Overall, the development of the marine transportation of liquefied gases has been a great commercial success. This is certainly due to the foresight of all the promoters of the industry and also to the excellence of the ship designers and operators, which allowed ships to work for many long years with an incomparable safety and performance record.

Roger Ffooks, one of the leading designers in the early years of LNG transport, was illustrating this good practice in one of his many fine papers, "Don't cheesepare in the design or construction of liquefied gas tankers; you will regret it sooner than you think". Although Roger's words were aimed at shipbuilders and owners concerned with building a new vessel, there is no doubt that he directed them equally to the issue of a ship's life-cycle cost. The patch-and-sail school of maintenance never had a serious audience in the industry. This is why owners are able today to sign, with confidence, long term charter parties for ships having already completed 25 years service or more. What a success!

6. LNG Tankers in Lay-up

Chapter 2
THE PRODUCTS

2.1 LIQUEFIED PETROLEUM GAS (LPG) - ORIGINS AND CHARACTERISTICS

Liquid Petroleum Gases, known as LPG, is the generic name used in the oil industry for butane (C_4H_{10}), propane (C_3H_8) or a mixture of the two. It describes odourless, non-toxic hydrocarbons which exist as a gas at normal atmospheric pressure and an ambient temperature of 15.6°C. These products are currently obtained by three methods:

- The treatment of crude oil to remove volatile components including methane, ethane, propane and butane. This process "stabilises" the crude oil prior to movement by pipeline or tanker.

- The refining of crude oil by distillation or cracking allows further amounts of butane and propane to be released from "stabilised" crude oil.

- The treatment of wet natural gas from natural gas or crude oil streams coming from underground reservoirs located within petroleum producing countries.

LPG manufactured from refinery cracked gases represents approximately 38% of global supplies, the remaining being extracted from the processing of associated or non-associated natural gas.

LPG is one of the cleanest fuels available for domestic, commercial or industrial markets, with a very low sulphur content. This is the main reason for its original development. However, several secondary usages have since generated large markets; i-butane and n-butane are important octane enhancers for motor gasoline and key petrochemical feedstocks. Propane is used as fuel for power generation, for industrial purposes and as petrochemical feedstock.

Liquefied Petroleum Gases are readily condensable to liquid at moderate pressures and temperatures. By liquefying the gas, its volume is reduced by a factor of 250. They are lighter than water when in liquid form with a density of 0.583 kg/m^3 for propane and approximately 0.600 kg/m^3 for butanes. They can be shipped in pressurised condition at ambient temperature or fully refrigerated at atmospheric pressure at temperatures of –0.5°C for n-butane, –11.7°C for i-butane and –42.3°C for propane. A mixture of 2.1 to 9.4% of propane and 1.8 to 8.5% of butanes gas in air can catch fire when in contact with a spark or a naked flame. When LPG is exposed to ambient temperature and atmospheric pressure, it vaporises quickly, and the gas is between 1.5 and 2 times heavier than air. LPG is colourless at ambient temperature and odourless.

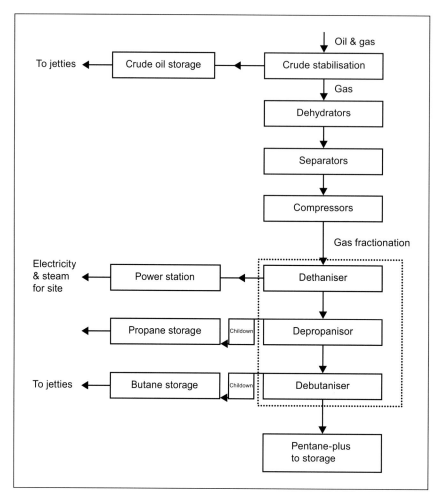

Figure 2.1 Typical Oil/Gas Flow Diagram. (SIGTTO.)

Liquefied gas	Vapour pressure at 37.8°C (bars absolute)	Boiling point at atmospheric pressure (°C)
Methane	Gas*	–161.5
Propane	12.9	–42.3
n-butane	3.6	–0.5
Ammonia	14.7	–33.4
Vinyl chloride	5.7	–13.8
Butadiene	4	–5
Ethylene oxide	2.7	10.7

* The critical temperature of methane is –82.5°C while the critical pressure is 44.7 bar. Therefore, at a temperature of 37.8°C it can only exist as a gas and not as a liquid.

Table 2.1 Physical Properties of some Liquid Gases. (SIGTTO.)

7. LPG Tanker. (The Author.)

The 1920's saw the first attempts to commercialise bottled LPG for domestic use. For many years, butanes and propane were transported in pressurised condition in relatively small quantities and were mainly used close to their production points. It was necessary to wait until the 1960's and the development of the refrigerated ship to see large scale expansion of marine transportation. This, in turn, allowed the recovery of large quantities of LPG available in remote oil production areas.

In 1997 the world-wide production of LPG was 179.6 million tonnes and approximately 47 million tonnes were traded internationally. This quantity is expected to increase to 62 million tonnes by year 2005.

2.2   LIQUEFIED NATURAL GAS (LNG) – ORIGIN AND CHARACTERISTICS

Liquid Natural Gas (LNG) is made up, for the most part, of Methane (CH_4), which accounts for between 75% and 95% of its volume. Natural gas is colourless at ambient temperature and it is also odourless and non-toxic.

Natural gas can be obtained from three different sources:

- Underground wells, which are mainly gas bearing (non-associated gas)
- Condensate reservoirs
- Large oil fields (associated gas)

In the case of associated gas, natural gas may be found either in solution with the crude oil or as a gas cap above it.

Natural gas contains smaller quantities of heavier hydrocarbons, in addition to varying amounts of water, carbon dioxide, hydrogen sulphide, nitrogen and other non-hydrocarbon substances. The constituents vary, depending on its geographical origin. It can comprise:

Methane		75% – 95%
Nitrogen		5% – 0.2%
Ethane	}	
Propane	}	1% – 25%
Butane	}	
Pentane	}	

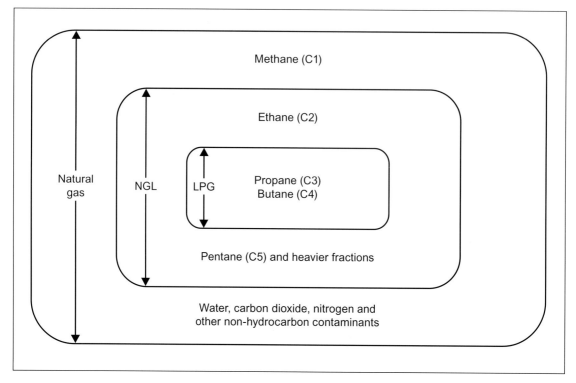

Figure 2.2 Constituents of Natural Gas. (SIGTTO.)

Natural gas is liquefied for shipping at a temperature of approximately -160°C. By liquefying the gas, its volume is reduced by a factor of 600, which means that LNG at -160°C uses 1/600 of the space required for the same weight of gas at ambient temperature. Hydrogen sulphide and carbon dioxide must be removed prior to liquefaction. This is generally referred to as gas sweetening.

LNG is a clear liquid, much lighter than water, with a density between 430 and 520 kg/dm³. A mixture of 5% to 14% of methane gas in air can ignite when in contact with a spark or naked flame.

When the liquid is loaded onto a ship, it immediately starts to "boil", or return to vapour form as it warms up by cooling the ship's containment system and from heat leakages through the tank insulation. The lighter constituents, having lower boiling points, vaporise first. Nitrogen, although having a higher molecular weight than methane, has a lower boiling point and forms a large part of the initial boil-off gas. The vapour phase of a tank can include up to 50% or more nitrogen in the initial hours after loading, depending on the composition of the LNG. This is important because, on LNG tankers, boil-off vapour is used as fuel in the ship's boiler. In this case, the usable combustible gas is reduced by the nitrogen content and the combustion control system must be designed to take this into account. Evaporation at different rates means that the gas delivered at the end of the voyage has a slightly lower proportion of nitrogen and methane than when loaded and a higher proportion of ethane, propane and butane.

When LNG is exposed to ambient temperature, as in the case of a leak, for example, it vaporises quickly. At liquid temperature, the gas is 1.4 times heavier than air, but, as it becomes warmer, its density decreases, reaching 0.55 times that of air at ambient temperature.

Natural gas has a calorific value higher than normal oil fuels but lower than LPG's, yet it is perceived as "clean". The combustion of natural gas releases lower amounts of soot, nitrogen oxides, sulphur oxides or carbon monoxide than other LPG, oil and solid fuels. The released amount of carbon dioxide is also lower than for other hydrocarbon fuels, at about 0.2 kg/kWh against 0.33 kg/kWh for coal and 0.26 kg/kWh for domestic fuel oil.

In 1997, almost 182 million cubic meters (or 82 million tonnes) of LNG were carried by sea and this is expected to rise to more than 100 million tonnes by 2005.

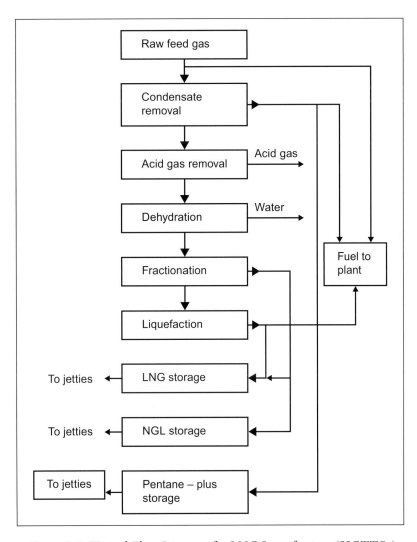

Figure 2.3 Typical Flow Diagram for LNG Liquefaction. (SIGTTO.)

9

8. LNG Loading Terminal. (The Author.)

2.3 LIQUEFIED PETROCHEMICAL GASES

2.3.1 GENERAL

A number of chemical gases or gases allied to or derived from within the petroleum industry have similar physical properties as LPG and are shipped on LPG carriers. They are commonly referred to as Liquefied Petrochemical Gases and can include ammonia (NH_3), butadiene (C_4H_6), propylene (C_3H_6), vinyl chloride monomer

(VCM) (C_2H_3Cl) and ethylene (C_2H_4). Petrochemical gases include other products but these five are the ones principally transported by sea and their origins and characteristics are described below.

2.3.2 AMMONIA (NH_3)

Ammonia is derived from synthesis gas by catalytic reforming, synthesis gas being produced by reforming water and a hydrocarbon such as coal, natural gas, petroleum gas or naphtha. The type of production process is thus determined by the feedstock available and this, in turn, determines the plant location. Natural gas forms the basis of approximately 80% of current production capacity.

Ammonia is a colourless gas with a characteristic pungent odour. It is very soluble in water; one volume of water will dissolve about 700 volumes of ammonia at 20°C. Anhydrous ammonia is readily condensable to liquid at moderate pressures and temperatures and is commonly known as liquid ammonia. In liquid form and at atmospheric pressure, ammonia is lighter than water, with a density of 0.680 kg/dm³. Ammonia can be shipped in pressurised condition at ambient temperature or fully refrigerated at atmospheric pressure at a temperature of –33.4°C. Ammonia is less flammable than other hydrocarbon gases; a mixture of ammonia gas in air is only flammable in the range of 14% to 27%, but it is poisonous and has a sharply irritating effect on the eyes, mucous membranes of the respiratory tract and on the moist areas of the skin. Below 60°C, Ammonia reacts with CO_2, to form ammonium carbamate, a white salt crust which adheres to the tank walls.

Ships carrying ammonia have to take special precautions to avoid any possibility of moisture contamination of the cargo as this can lead to the phenomenon of stress corrosion cracking which can be very damaging to the cargo tanks.

In 1997, world-wide production of ammonia was 120 million tonnes, of which approximately 10% was internationally traded. This quantity has been stable during recent years.

2.3.3 BUTADIENE (C_4H_6)

Butadiene is one of the olefins group and 90% of production is used by the rubber industry. It is also used in paints and binders for non-woven fabrics and as an intermediary in plastic and nylon production. Butadiene is mainly obtained by extraction from crude C4 streams produced as a by-product of ethylene manufacture and refinery operations. It can also be obtained from the dehydrogenation of n-butane and from ethyl alcohol.

Butadiene is a colourless gas with a strangely aromatic odour. It is slightly poisonous but strongly carcinogenic. In high concentrations, it irritates the skin and acts as an anaesthetic. It is easily condensable to liquid at moderate pressures and temperatures.

In liquid form and at atmospheric pressure, it is lighter than water with a density of 0.650 kg/dm³. Brought into contact with air, butadiene readily forms peroxides, which do not dissolve in liquid butadiene. These peroxides are very sensitive to heat and to impact and can lead to uncontrollable explosions. Heat, short-wave or the presence of peroxides or other agents can polymerise the butadiene, producing, in the liquid phase, a dark rubber-like polymer and, in the gas phase, white crystals. For these reasons, butadiene is mainly shipped in a fully refrigerated condition at atmospheric pressure at a temperature of –5°C, with the addition of stabilisers to prevent polymerisation. Mixtures of 2% to 11.5% of butadiene gas in air can ignite when in contact with a spark or a naked gas flame.

In 1997, world-wide production of butadiene was more than 8 million tonnes, of which approximately 800,000 tonnes were transported by sea.

2.3.4 PROPYLENE (C_3H_6)

Propylene is also one of the olefins group and is polymerised into polypropylene, which is used in the manufacture of moulded components for cars and domestic appliances, carpet fibres, cable sheathing, piping, coatings and containers. Propylene is mainly produced as a by-product of ethylene (70%) but it can also be produced by refineries (29%) or through propane dehydrogenation (1%), a process which should see a considerable development due to the expected deficit in propylene forecast for the near future.

Propylene is a colourless gas with narcotic properties which burns in air with a yellow soot-forming flame. In high concentrations, it has a slight and strange odour. It is easily condensable to liquid at moderate pressures and temperatures. In liquid form and at atmospheric pressure, it is lighter than water, with a density of 0.612 kg dm³. Propylene can be shipped in pressurised condition at ambient temperature or fully refrigerated at atmospheric pressure at a temperature of –47.7°C. Mixtures of 2.2% to 10.2% of propylene gas in air can ignite when in contact with a spark or a naked flame.

In 1996, world-wide production of propylene was 41 million tonnes and approximately 2.7 million tonnes were transported by sea.

2.3.5 VINYL CHLORIDE MONOMER (VCM) (C_2H_3CL)

VCM is produced by the oxychlorination process which treats ethylene to produce ethylene dichloride which then gives VCM through pyrolysis or by reaction with caustic soda. It can also be produced from acetylene and hydrogen chloride. VCM is mainly used in the production of plastics (polyvinylchlorides or PVC).

Vinyl Chloride Monomer is a colourless, slightly poisonous gas. In high concentration, it has a pleasant, sweet odour and acts as a narcotic. VCM is a strong carcinogenic agent. It is easily condensable to liquid at moderate pressures and temperatures. In liquid form and at atmospheric pressure, it is almost as heavy as water, with a density of 0.97 kg/dm³. Vinyl chloride decomposes in an open flame and gives phosgenes. VCM can be shipped in pressurised condition at ambient temperature or fully refrigerated at atmospheric pressure at a temperature of –13.8°C. Mixtures of 4% to 29.3% of VCM gas in air can be inflamed by contact with a spark or a naked flame.

In 1996, world-wide production of VCM was more than 22 million tonnes of which 786,000 tonnes were transported by sea.

9. A Refinery. (SIGTTO.)

2.3.6 ETHYLENE (C_2H_4)

Ethylene is one of the most basic components of the petrochemical industry. Its production involves "cracking" a suitable feedstock such as ethane, propane, butane, naphtha or gasoil into ethylene and several other co-products including propylene and butadiene. Ethylene is polymerised into high density polyethylene (HDPE), low density polyethylene (LDPE) and linear low density polyethylene (LLDPE) which, in turn, are used to make plastic packaging, films, bottles, containers and household hardware. Ethylene glycol, used as antifreeze, is produced by oxidation and hydration. Ethylene is used with benzene in the manufacture of styrene to produce polystyrene for insulation, packaging and toys.

Ethylene is a colourless, practically odourless and slightly poisonous gas. As an olefin, it is more narcotic than lower paraffin (propane, butane). Ethylene burns in air with a soot-forming red luminous flame. It is condensable to liquid at a very low temperature. In liquid form at atmospheric pressure, it is lighter than water, with a density of 0.570 kg/dm³. Ethylene can be shipped either in fully refrigerated condition at atmospheric pressure at a temperature of –103.9°C or under a pressure of about 5 bars at a temperature of approximately –75°C.

Gas	Atmospheric boiling point (°C)	Critical temperature (°C)	Critical pressure (bar, abs.)	Condensing ratio dm³ liquid/ m³ gas	Liquid relative density at Atm. boiling pt. (Water = 1)	Vapour relative density (Air = 1)
Methane	–161.5	–82.5	44.7	0.804	0.427	0.554
Ethane	–88.6	32.1	48.9	2.453	0.54	1.048
Propane	–42.3	96.8	42.6	3.38	0.583	1.55
n–Butane	–0.5	153	38.1	4.32	0.6	2.09
i-Butane	–11.7	133.7	38.2	4.36	0.596	2.07
Ethylene	–103.9	9.9	50.5	2.2	0.57	0.975
Propylene	–47.7	92.1	45.6	3.08	0.613	1.48
α–Butylene	–6.1	146.4	38.9	4.01	0.624	1.94
y–Butylene	–6.9	144.7	38.7	4	0.627	1.94
Butadiene	–5	161.8	43.2	3.81	0.653	1.88
Isoprene	34	211	38.5		0.67	2.3
Vinyl chloride	–13.8	158.4	52.9	2.87	0.965	2.15
Ethylene oxide	10.7	195.7	74.4	2.13	0.896	1.52
Propylene oxide	34.2	209.1	47.7		0.83	2
Ammonia	–33.4	132.4	113	1.12	0.683	0.597
Chlorine	–34	144	77.1	2.03	1.56	2.49

Table 2.2 Physical Properties of Gases. (SIGTTO.)

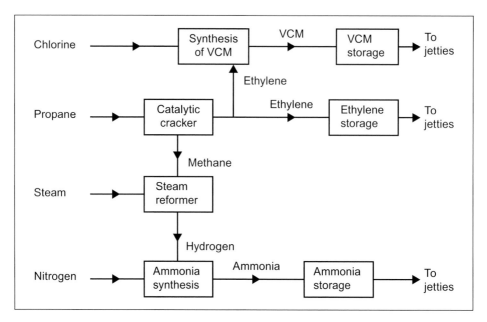

Figure 2.4 Typical Flow Diagram – Production of Chemical Gases. (SIGTTO.)

Because of this low temperature, it is necessary to have special ships for the transportion of ethylene. A mixture of 2.7% to 28.5% of ethylene gas in air can ignite when in contact with a spark or naked flame.

In 1996 the world-wide production of ethylene was more than 75 million tonnes of which approximately 3 million tonnes were transported by sea.

10. Semi Pressurised LPG Tanker. (SIGTTO.)

Chapter 3
HISTORY

3.1 LIQUEFIED PETROLEUM GAS (LPG)

3.1.1 THE BEGINNING

In 1911, Dr. Walter O'Snelling of the U.S. Bureau of Mines succeeded in separating and liquefying butane and propane. He patented his discoveries in 1913.

Industrial production of propane and butane by Union Carbide and Carbon Chemicals started in the 1920's, in the USA. The gas was mainly for domestic use and was delivered to the customers in pressurised bottles. It was transported overland in larger pressurised bottles installed on trucks. The expeditions of Adm. R. Byrd to the South Pole in 1929 and 1934 used bottles of compressed gas for their cooking fuel.

Butane and propane were first transported by sea in the 1930's on a small number of general cargo ships equipped with pressurised bottles on deck. The first attempt to transport LPG by sea using a purpose-built ship took place in 1931, when the Hawthorn Leslie shipyard (now Swan Hunter) designed and built the m.v. "Agnita" for the Anglo Saxon Petroleum Company in London (now Shell International Trading and Shipping). Twelve riveted tanks installed vertically in the cargo holds enabled the ship to carry pressurised butane and sulphuric acid. The normal oil cargo was carried around the butane tanks. The "Agnita" operated without problems until 1941, when she was sunk by a torpedo. A second sister-ship was built, but noticeable developments took place only after the war.

In 1947, a dry-cargo ship, the "Natalie O. Warren" was converted by the Bethlehem Steel Company of Beaumont, Texas for the Warren Petroleum Corporation, to carry propane from Houston to New York and renamed "Cape Diamond". She was fitted with 68 vertical, cylindrical tanks with a maximum working pressure of 17.6 kg/cm^2 and a total cargo capacity of 6,050 m^3. The tanks had diameters of 2.4 to 4.0 m and heights between 7.6 and 14.6 m and were installed in 5 holds. A second vessel, the "Rio Novo", was converted by the same shipyard a year later for the owner Oivind Lorentzen of Norway. This owner had previously equipped dry-cargo ships with deck-mounted skid tanks to carry LPG from the US Gulf to Brazil. The "Rio Novo" was fitted with 29 vertical and 2 horizontal tanks, with a total capacity of 3,000 m^3 and a working pressure of 17.5 kg/cm^2, in order to carry butane and propane. She was the first real sea-going LPG tanker. Two other ships were also converted for the same owner in 1952-53 in the Kieler Howaldtswerke shipyard of West Germany: the "Mundogas Sao Paulo" and the "Mundogas Norte".

All these ship conversions used the same techniques as those used for the overland transportation of LPG. The large number of small prefabricated tanks and complicated piping network made the ships cumbersome.

At the end of the war, there was a demand in Europe for the transportation of LPG between various coastal regions. A number of shipyards in Italy, Sweden, Denmark, Holland and France started to build small, specially designed, pressurised LPG tankers.

In Italy, Genoa's C.N.Ansaldo shipyard delivered the 670 m³ "Mariotte" in 1946 and the 1850 m³ "Agipgas Quarta", with 18 vertical tanks, in 1952. The Felszegi yard in Trieste delivered the 212 m³ "Elpigas" in 1947 to SNAM S.p.A. The C.N. Benetti yard in Viareggio delivered the 1,730 m³ "Agipgas Terza" in 1959.

In Sweden, the Marstrands shipyard delivered the 1,042 m³, "Rasmus Tholstrup" with 12 vertical cylindrical tanks, which was the first of 23 Tholstrup LPG tankers.

In Denmark, the A/S Svendborg shipyard delivered the "Soerine Tholstrup" with a single horizontal tank of 1750 m³, in 1954.

Also in 1954, the Muller-Foxal shipyard in Holland delivered the 816 m³ "Cap Carbon" to the French owner SAGA, to transport LPG from Berre, France to Arzew, Algeria or to Corsica.

In 1960, the France-Gironde shipyard in France delivered the 1,554 m³ "Cap Ferrat", also to SAGA.

In Japan, the beginning of the 1960's saw a substantial requirement for coastal transport of LPG and more than 130 small pressurised ships were built by Japanese shipyards for various Japanese owners. In 1965, Mitsubishi Heavy Industries shipyard delivered two 2,080 m³ ships equipped with four spherical tanks, "Kegums" and "Kraslava", for the USSR. At the time, this was quite an unusual design.

11. Two Pressurised Ships in Dry Dock. (The Author.)

16

Most ships built during this period had a total capacity below 2000 m³ and were designed with a minimum cargo temperature of –5°C for the transportation of butane, propane, butadiene and ammonia at ambient temperature. The maximum service pressure was between 17 and 18 bar gauge. Discharge was carried out using compressors, sometimes with the assistance of a booster pump. The quality of welding technology and the material available did not allow for tanks with a capacity larger than 600 m³, which meant the ships had to be equipped with a number of smaller tanks connected by a complicated piping network. However, fully pressurised LPG ships were the only type available through the 1950's and they became quite popular. They were simple reliable ships and enjoyed a good safety record.

The improved availability of low temperature steel, the better knowledge of its forming and welding and the improvement of refrigeration plants suitable for on-board installation helped the development of different types of ships.

When carried at a lower temperature, the cargo pressure is reduced and its specific gravity is increased. As the pressure is reduced, cargo tanks do not require the same thickness and consequently their weight and the weight of their supports are reduced. All this allows more cargo to be carried for the same size of ship and therefore more revenue can be earned. However, to achieve this result, it is necessary to use better quality steel for the cargo tanks and to provide insulation and special equipment to maintain the cargo at a lower temperature.

Semi-pressurised ships appeared first. Early designs transported the cargo at pressures between 5 and 9 bar, but their minimum temperatures were still limited to –5 or –10°C. This soon improved with minimum temperatures as low as –48°C becoming available. It enabled the new ships to carry all the products described above

at very nearly their atmospheric pressures. They were now capable of loading fully refrigerated cargoes which they could discharge at ambient temperature through a system of cargo heaters or to load cargoes at ambient temperature which they could cool down at sea and discharge at near atmospheric pressure. This increased greatly their flexibility and the range of cargoes available for transportation. Most of these ships were equipped to carry two and sometimes more different products, completely segregated.

Fully-refrigerated ships followed soon after. They could transport all the same products at near atmospheric pressure and at the same low temperatures. Because their maximum pressure was limited to 0.7 bar, the weight of their cargo containment was greatly reduced and larger ships became feasible.

The first semi-pressurised ships appeared at the end of the 1950's. They were the 921 m³ "Descartes" in France, the 920 m³ "Lili Tholstrup" and "Birthe Tholstrup" in Denmark, seven 2,000 m³ built in Spain, the 754 m³ "Abbas" in the UK, a modified bulk carrier which become one of the largest semi-pressurised ships at the time, the 13,196 m³ "Cap Martin" in France and many others. The 6,327 m³ "Pascal", built in 1967 by Chantiers Naval de la Ciotat in France, was the first ship able to load semi-pressurised or fully refrigerated cargoes.

The first fully-refrigerated LPG ship was built in 1961 by the Mitsubishi Heavy Industries shipyard of Yokohama, Japan. The cargo containment system was designed by J.J. Henry Co. Inc. based in New York, using Conch International Methane Technology. She was "Bridgestone Maru No 1", with four prismatic independent type A tanks of 28,875 m³ total capacity, with a minimum temperature of –45°C. The inner hull was constructed of 2¼% Ni steel and the tanks of 3½% Ni steel. This was certainly above requirements, by today's standards, for the

12. Pressurised LPG Tanker. (SIGTTO.)

13. Semi pressurised LPG Tanker.

cargoes considered. The insulation was glassfibre, attached to the inner hull surfaces and protected by aluminium foil. The design was a direct result of the experiments recently completed on LNG transportation in the United States by Conch International assisted by J.J. Henry.

This design introduced the new concept of a secondary barrier, made of steel able to maintain its mechanical properties when in contact with the low temperature of the cargo, to protect the ship's hull from possible damage due to this low temperature in case of leaks in the primary cargo containment system.

Two years later, the first fully-refrigerated LPG tanker built in Europe was delivered by the Kockums shipyard in Sweden. This was the 25,012 m³ "Paul Endacott", designed to carry LPG, NH_3, or ethylene oxide in five self-supporting prismatic tanks at a minimum temperature of –51°C. Four different products could be carried and refrigerated simultaneously at a maximum pressure of 0.3 bar. The tank material was low carbon high tensile steel. The polyurethane foam insulation was bonded to the inner part of the hull, to allow for easy inspection of the tanks. The ballast tanks were located in way of the cargo tanks within the hull's double skin. Four pressurised tanks, with a total capacity of 1,216 m³, were installed on deck to facilitate purging and pre-cooling whilst on passage.

In the same year, the Verolme shipyard in the Netherlands delivered the 12,975 m³ "William R. Grace", specifically designed to carry fully refrigerated ammonia between Trinidad and the US Gulf or Europe. Two sister-ships would be delivered to the same owner, the Oswego Chemical Carrier Corp.

Also in that year, the MHI shipyard of Yokohama, Japan, delivered the 36,000 m³ "Bridgestone Maru No 2". This design, very similar to the standard which would be used for most of the fully-refrigerated LPG ships to come, uses the inner hull and part of the side shell itself as the secondary barrier.

3.1.2 DEVELOPMENT

The 1960's saw very fast development of all types of LPG tankers. Further developments in steel quality and welding technology allowed the size of fully pressurised cargo tanks to be increased and many ships in that category were built with a capacity of 3 to 5,000 m³ even reaching 10,000 m³. Modern fully-pressurised ships are equipped with several spherical or cylindrical tanks with a maximum service pressure of 17 or 18 bar gauge and a minimum temperature of –5°C. Some fully-pressurised ships are now fitted with tanks able to carry cargo at temperatures as low as –25°C, which increases their flexibility even further. Some ships can carry two different products completely separated and discharging is done using compressors and centrifugal booster pumps.

For the same reasons, cargo tanks on semi-pressurised ships were able to carry cargoes at temperatures of –50°C and, very soon, ethylene ships able to withstand temperatures of –104°C became available. The parallel development of shipboard reliquefaction equipment was also instrumental in ensuring these changes. Semi-pressurised ships saw their sizes increase to 20,000 or even 25,000 m³. They became extremely flexible, able to carry many different products, often several, completely separated at the same time, and even chemical products, when the opportunity arose.

14. Modern Pressurised LPG Tanker. (SIGTTO.)

15. Semi Pressurised LPG Tanker. (The Author.)

16. Fully Refrigerated LPG Tanker, (The Author.)

Finally, improvements in ship design, combined with those listed on the previous page, allowed the size of fully refrigerated ships to be increased to 50,000, 70,000, 80,000 and even 100,000 m³. A limited number of owners have specialised in operating big fleets of these large fully refrigerated ships, which are usually working on long term charters.

3.1.3 LIQUEFIED PETROCHEMICAL GASES

Most liquefied petrochemical gases have physical properties very similar to those of propane and butane and can be transported by the same types of ships. Prior to the 1960's, however, only small quantities of ammonia and even smaller quantities of butadiene were transported in fully-pressurised ships. The development of the more flexible semi-pressurised and fully-refrigerated ships saw a large increase in the liquefied petrochemical gas trade. Ammonia is transported in large quantities, mainly in fully refrigerated ships. Other products, such as butadiene, propylene and vinyl chloride monomer are transported in semi-pressurised ships. Some very dangerous products, such as chlorine, are also transported in small quantities in specially equipped semi-pressurised ships because of the increased safety provided by such vessels. Ethylene, due to its different characteristics, requires specially designed ships.

3.1.4   ETHYLENE TANKERS

The latest type of LPG ship to appear on the market was the ethylene tanker. Ethylene, with a temperature of −104°C at atmospheric pressure and a critical temperature close to 10°C (the temperature at which a gas cannot be liquefied by pressure alone), requires to be transported in refrigerated condition either fully refrigerated or at a pressure of a few bars. Special materials are required for the cargo containment system, such as 5% nickel steel or aluminium. The reliquefaction equipment needs also some special specifications, different from those used on normal LPG ships.

Ethylene is an important base chemical, used extensively in the plastics industry. It is, however, transported in much smaller quantities than LPG. The main trading routes are in Europe, North and South America, India, the Far East, Japan and Korea.

The first ships designed specifically to carry Ethylene were built in the UK by Burntisland Shipbuilding for George Gibson & Co in 1966. They were the 826 m³ "Teviot" and "Traquair". The tanks were built of aluminium-magnesium

alloy with insulation of expanded polyurethane foam covered with glass-fibre reinforced plastic to form the secondary barrier. This design was unfortunately not accepted by the IMO Gas Code implemented at the end of the 1970's, which requires a full double hull for this type of ship.

Several of the ethylene tankers in service today are either small prototypes of various LNG tanker designs built to demonstrate the validity of the design or even small LNG ships equipped with the necessary reliquefaction equipment. However, they are a small minority in this category of ship, which now includes more than 150 vessels. The typical, modern ethylene tanker is a semi-pressurised ship of 10,000 to 15,000 m³ capacity, with IMO type C bi-lobe self supporting tanks designed to carry the cargo fully refrigerated at a temperature of −104°C or under a moderate pressure of 5 or 6 bar.

17. Ethylene Tanker. (The Author.)

3.2   LIQUEFIED NATURAL GAS (LNG)

3.2.1   THE BEGINNING

Although the first attempts at air liquefaction were made at the end of the last century, the first liquefied methane was only obtained by the

US Bureau of Mines in 1924, as a by-product of helium separation. The use of liquefied gas for distribution by the gas industry was first proposed in the United States in the 1930's; but, it was 1940 before the first liquefaction plant for peak shaving was built. Further construction of peak shaving facilities followed until a major accident and disastrous fire at the Cleveland LNG storage plant, in 1944, set back LNG peak shaving development by several years. No further commercial plants were in fact built in the US until the early sixties, though, a large liquefaction plant was supplied by the US to the USSR and installed in Moscow in 1947.

Early in the 1950's, the Union Stock Yards of Chicago thought of liquefying natural gas in Louisiana, where it was available in large quantities, and transporting the LNG by barge up the Mississippi River to Chicago, to be used as fuel by the meat industry. A small liquefaction plant and LNG storage tank were built at Lake Charles, Louisiana, as well as a 6,000 m³ barge called "Methane". For technical reasons, the project was abandoned and no LNG was shipped to Chicago. But, several years later, this plant was to produce the LNG for the first seven transatlantic cargoes transported by "Methane Pioneer".

At that time, the British Gas Council was looking at ways to supplement the production of manufactured gas, which was becoming insufficient due to the reduction in coal mining. In 1957, Constock Liquid Methane Corporation, a joint venture between Union Stock Yard and Continental Oil Co, signed an agreement with the British Gas Council to convert a World War II dry cargo vessel, "m.v. Normati", into a 5,000 m³ LNG tanker.

In February 1959, the converted vessel, renamed "Methane Pioneer", transported the first LNG cargo from Lakes Charles, Louisiana to the UK where it was discharged at the Canvey Island methane terminal in the Thames estuary. Six further cargoes were similarly transported and discharged, to complete this successful experimental project. The vessel was owned jointly by the British Gas Council and Constock and the conversion was designed by Constock Liquid Methane Co. assisted by J.J. Henry Company, naval architects, New York City. The work followed the requirements and was subject to the approval of the American Bureau of Shipping and Lloyd's Register of Shipping and was supervised by the US Coast Guard.

The five cargo tanks were of prismatic shape, built of aluminium alloy 5356-0 and the insulation was made of prefabricated sandwich-type panels of balsa wood faced with maple and oak plywood attached to the inner hull. These were the forerunners of the self-supporting prismatic IMO type B tank, before the concept was even invented. All deck piping was of stainless steel TP 304 L.

Following the successful results obtained by "Methane Pioneer", Shell Petroleum joined Constock in 1960 and the new group became the Conch Methane Company Limited, later known more simply as Conch.

Similar work was carried out in France to provide a way of transporting the natural gas just discovered in Algeria. The Methane Transport Company was formed in 1959, under the driving force of Gaz de France, to co-ordinate the work done by several shipyards. A wartime liberty-ship, "Beauvais", was made available for conversion and three tanks of different shapes, designed by three different shipyards and groups of shipyards, were made and installed on board. The first one, with a capacity of 400 m³, was prismatic, made of aluminium AG-4, with a secondary barrier in fibreglass; the second one, with a capacity of 120 m³, was a multi-lobe shape, made of 9%

18. "Methane Pioneer". (SIGTTO.)

nickel steel and enclosed in a steel casing; the third tank, with a capacity of 120 m³, was a vertical cylinder with a conical bottom and an elliptical top, the internal tank made of aluminium AG-4 and an outer tank, of the same shape, made of 9% nickel steel. The insulation for all three tanks consisted of PVC blocks mixed with perlite. The piping was stainless steel and three different types of cargo pump were used, two deepwell types and one Carter pump with submerged electric motor. The conversion was completed in February 1962, under the supervision of Bureau Veritas with the participation of the Lloyd's Register of Shipping. Six months of extensive tests followed, to prove the good performance of the tanks and other equipment.

In February 1962, the British Gas Corporation placed an order for two ships, to provide transportation for the 15-year contract signed with Algeria for 100 million cubic feet/day of natural gas. They were "Methane Princess" and "Methane Progress", each of 27,400 m³ capacity, ordered from Vickers Shipbuilders, Barrow-in-Furness and Harland & Wolff, Belfast. The two ships were of the Conch design, with prismatic self-supporting cargo tanks made of 5083-0 aluminium alloy, with insulation made of combined balsa wood and glass fibre acting as a secondary barrier. The ships were jointly classed by A.B.S and L.R.S. The boil-off was designed at 0.33% of the total cargo capacity per day and these were the first ships to use the cargo boil-off as fuel for the boilers. Both ships were delivered to their owner in 1964. "Methane Progress" was sold for scrap after 22 years of successful service. In 1997, the decision to sell "Methane Princess" for scrap, after 32 years of service, was taken, not because of the condition of the ship, but because her size made her uneconomical in the existing market.

At the same time, in France, the 25,500 m³ capacity "Jules Verne" was ordered by Gaz Marine, a joint venture between Gaz de France, Gazocean, Bennett Corporation and a number of banks, from Ateliers et Chantiers de la Seine Maritime. The ship was delivered in 1965 and was contracted to carry LNG from Arzew, Algeria, to the Gaz de France terminal at Le Havre for 20 years. The seven cargo tanks were of vertical cylindrical shape with a conical bottom and an elliptical top and made of 9% nickel steel. They were internally stiffened with six internal rings. The insulation was a combination of Klegecell and perlite in bulk and a secondary insulation of

Klegecell covered with a liquid-tight aluminium-textile complex served as a secondary barrier. The boil-off was designed at 0.27% of the total cargo capacity per day and was used as fuel for the boilers. "Jules Verne" is still operating regularly between Algeria and Spain, after 34 years service and almost 1200 voyages.

"Methane Progress", "Methane Princess" and "Jules Verne" were all equipped with submerged electrical motor pumps, fitted with some apprehension as to their reliability but which proved trouble-free in service. Despite having been supplied with very carefully written operating manuals and substantial crew training, the three ships have suffered some spillage and overflow of cargo, causing cracked decks, but the resulting damage was minimal. The three ships also suffered some small amounts of inner hull leakage which eventually required some loss of time for repairs, but which did not affect the quality of the tank insulation.

19. "Methane Princess". (SIGTTO.)

Further research was being carried out during this period. In 1954, in Norway, Dr Oivind Lorentzen designed a ship of 17,000 m³ capacity equipped with spherical tanks and the project received approval from Det Norske Veritas.

Many naval architects of the time did not think that the self-supporting tanks used for the first LNG tankers were the best solution. The hull of a ship is designed and built to transport bulk cargoes and this was well demonstrated by the success of oil and ore carriers. This gave ship designers the idea of replacing the self-supporting tanks, which required large amounts of expensive cryogenic alloy, with a cryogenic protection covering the internal surface of the ship's hold. This would allow optimal use of the full volume available and the possibility to transport more cargo due to the reduction of dead weight.

In July 1962, in Oslo, a demonstration of a shore tank using the membrane principle was organised. The concept had been invented by an engineer from Det Norske Veritas and acquired by Dr Oivind Lorentzen, a ship-owner associated with Carol Bennett, a Texas-based oilman, both of whom were interested in the transportation of liquefied gas by sea. The membrane, made of aluminium alloy, had been designed with orthogonal corrugations able to sustain extensive movements in two perpendicular directions under a light load. The insulation used a combination of rock-wool and wood. All present at the demonstration were impressed by the tests consisting of repeated filling of the 32 m³ tank with liquid nitrogen at –196°C without any special pre-cooling.

20. "Jules Verne". (The Author.)

21. Drawing of "Jules Verne" Tank. (The Author.)

After long and arduous negotiations, the French company Technigaz, a subsidiary of Gazocean, acquired the Norwegian licence. Following a new programme of research, a lot of changes were introduced to the basic design. The membrane was changed to low carbon stainless steel, the shape and pitch of the corrugations were altered and the insulation was PVC foam. In 1964, a small 630 m³ LNG/Ethylene tanker, "Pythagore", was built to successfully demonstrate the good operation of the system. The ship remained mainly in ethylene and LPG service until converted to a fish transporter in 1973.

Another system of membrane was developed by a French group led by Gaz de France including other French interests. The material used for the membrane was a nickel-steel alloy with 36% nickel licensed by the IMPHY company in 1896 under the name of "Invar" for "invariable". Invar was created by Professor Guillaume, who received the Nobel Prize for physics and this material has a very small shrinkage factor. Due to this minimum shrinkage, the thermal stresses

induced in the material by the very cold cargo temperature were low enough to allow its use in flat streaks to provide the required sealing function between cargo and ship's hull. A second membrane, symmetrical to the first one, acted as the secondary barrier. The insulation was provided by two layers of plywood boxes filled with perlite. A small 30 m³ tank was installed on the "Jules Verne" for testing purposes and used for several months to carry liquid nitrogen. Then, a 2,000 m³ LNG experimental shore storage tank was built by Gaz de France. A company named Gas Transport was created in 1965 to continue this project. A 30,000 m³ LPG carrier was ordered by the Worms group from Construction Navales et Industrielles de la Mediterranee in 1967. For the minimum temperature of –45°C specified for this ship, one layer of insulation was sufficient. Otherwise, the specifications of the cargo containment system were the same as those for LNG. The ship was delivered at the beginning of 1969 and traded successfully until 1974 when she was converted to a Ro-ro.

3.2.2 DEVELOPMENT

The end of the 1960's saw the start of two important LNG projects.

In the final weeks of 1965, Esso signed an agreement with Libya, Italy and Spain to deliver respectively 235 MMSCF and 110 MMSCF per day of natural gas. This project, due to start in 1968, required four ships of approximately 40,000 m³ capacity and 18 knot service speed. After careful review of the LNG containment systems available, their relative costs, licensing conditions and potential reliability in service, Esso decided to develop their own independent, prismatic, self-supporting tank design. They opted for a double-wall, longitudinally divided aluminium tank. The insulation, comprising an assembly of PVC blocks in two layers, with glass fibre fitted between adjacent blocks to accommodate the expansion and contraction of the tanks, was attached to the outer tank shell. Three ships were ordered from the Italcantieri shipyard in Genoa and one from the Astano yard in El Ferrol, near La Coruna in western Spain. All four ships were fitted with Carter submerged pumps, two per tank, giving a total combined discharge rate of 4,000 m³/hour. Each tank was equipped with a valve in the longitudinal bulkhead to enable each pump to discharge the whole tank in case of pump failure. The first ship, "Esso Brega", entered service in October 1969, the second, "Esso Portovenere" in March 1970 and the third and fourth "Laieta" and "Esso Liguria" later the same year. "Esso Portovenere" was sold for scrap in 1982 but the other three ships are still in service today.

The first contract to import LNG to Japan was signed in the spring of 1967 between two American companies, Phillips Petroleum and Marathon Oil, on one side and Mitsubishi Corporation and Tokyo Electric Power Corp on the other. The contract involved the delivery of 1.1 million tonnes of LNG per year from Kenai Nikiski in Alaska to Negishi in the Tokyo Bay. Two ships were ordered from the Kockums shipyard in Malmo, Sweden. The new Gas Transport Invar membrane system was selected as the tank design. The two ships, "Polar Alaska" and "Arctic Tokyo" entered service in November 1969 and March 1970 respectively. After 25 years service on that particularly demanding route, the two ships are still successfully trading world-wide and will enter new long-term commitments in the near future.

During the seventies and eighties, a number of other projects involving many ships of various designs were started. Some of these projects had a very short life span and some never materialised at all, leaving a number of ships without employment. Some ships were built but remained in lay-up for more than 20 years without ever carrying a commercial cargo. Other ships were very successfully employed and will probably continue to be so for many years to come. It is worth noting that, although a small number of LNG ships have been scrapped over the years, the decision has always been taken for commercial reasons and not due to the ship's poor performance or deterioration. The exception to this is a series of three ships built in the United States at the end of the seventies, with Conch design tanks. The material selected for the secondary barrier never performed to the required standard and the ships were eventually converted into coal carriers.

The size of LNG ships has increased very quickly, from the 27,400 m³ of "Methane Princess" and "Methane Progress" to reach 125,000 m³ in the middle of the 1970's and this capacity remained as a standard for many years. It is only recently that sizes have crept up slightly to 138,000 m³ and, for the time being, there are no serious prospects to go much higher.

22. "Polar Alaska".

Another interesting point is that LNG ships, even those ordered in 1999, are consistently specified with steam turbine propulsion. This is the least efficient ship propulsion mode available today, but it survives due to its reputation for great reliability and for providing an easy disposal of the boil-off. Shipyards have suggested various other propulsion systems, such as slow diesel engines combined with reliquefaction plants or diesel-electric systems with medium speed gas burning diesel engines, but, so far, no owner has been bold enough to take advantage of such developments.

23. Spherical Tank LNG Tanker. (The Author.)

24. LNG Tanker of the Gaz Transport Membrane Type. (The Author.)

25. *LNG Tanker of the SPB Tank Type. (IHI.)*

26. *LNG Tanker of the Technigaz Membrane Type. (GTT.)*

Chapter 4
THE INTERNATIONAL TRADE

4.1   LIQUEFIED PETROLEUM AND PETROCHEMICAL GASES

4.1.1   THE FLEET

The LPG fleet started with pressurised ships of less than 5,000 m³ capacity. The first semi-pressurised ships were delivered at the end of the 1950's and sizes in this category did not go much above 10,000 m³ before the 1970's. The first fully-refrigerated ships appeared in the 1960's but it was in the 1970's that the first 50,000 m³ vessels were delivered.

Fifty-two gas tankers were either converted or newly-built prior to 1960 and another 233 between 1961 and 1968. In 1970, the fleet included more than 220 ships under 2,000 m³, approximately 80 vessels between 2,000 and 10,000 m³ and 50 vessels of more than 10,000 m³. At the end of 1998, the situation had changed substantially and the fleet comprised 444 pressurised vessels of less than 10,000 m³, 276 semi-pressurised vessels and 186 fully refrigerated vessels.

In 1973, pressurised vessels accounted for 63% of the total number of ships and 9.5% of the total capacity and refrigerated vessels made up 4.5% of the total number but already almost 20% of the total capacity. At the end of 1997, pressurised vessels accounted for 49% of the total number of ships but only 7.3% of the total capacity. By then, refrigerated vessels only accounted for 20.5% of the total number of ships but 78.6% of the total capacity.

Chart 4.1 and Table 4.1 show the evolution of the fleet over the years and Table 4.2 shows the situation at the end of 1997. Table 4.3 shows the number of ships on order at the end of 1997.

Normal LPG ships are also used for the transport of ammonia and other petrochemical gases, such as propylene, butadiene and vinyl chloride monomer. Special cargo containment systems, resistant to very low temperatures, are required for the transport of ethylene, but the ships used for this trade are, except for this specific point, of a basic design similar to other LPG ships. All different types of LPG tankers are able to carry ammonia or propylene, butadiene or VCM and most of the existing ships have done so at one time or another. The very cumbersome tank cleaning operation required between a cargo of ammonia and the next cargo of LPG or other chemical gas does not make ammonia the ship operators' favourite product. However, it is better to carry ammonia than to have a ship unemployed. Some ships are dedicated to ammonia and do not carry any other cargo for long periods. LPG tankers tend to be designed for flexible operation, to have the possibility to carry a maximum number of different cargoes under different conditions of pressure and temperature.

Despite the uncertainty of the trade, the fleet of liquefied gas tankers is following a regular progression, with the number of ships increasing by 4.9% per year during the period 1990 to 1997.

The range of size of the different types of ships has not changed much over the past twenty years and seems set for the foreseeable future.

	Number of Ships	Total Capacity (1000 m³)
1940	2	1
1950	15	20
1960	50	130
1973	350	2340
1976	414	3606
1983	630	7200
1990	680	8100
1997	906	12485

Table 4.1 Growth of World LPG Fleet to End 1997. (Clarkson.)

Most liquefied gas tankers continue trading well beyond their 20th year and some even longer. This does not allow for a large number of new buildings. However shipyards around the world are keen to tender for liquefied gas carriers. In addition to those countries and regions traditionally specialising in building such vessels, Europe, Japan and more recently South Korea, the shipyards of countries new to the industry, such as China and India, are starting to acquire a reputation for the construction of these specialised tankers.

If the example of previous years is anything to go by, as soon as a balance is reached between

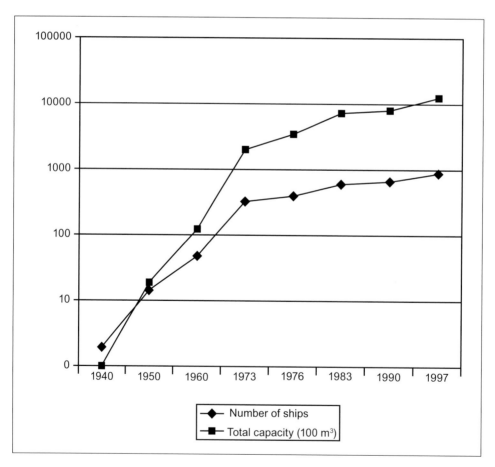

Chart 4.1 Growth of World LPG Fleet to End 1997.

the number of ships available and the number of ships in demand, owners start a flurry of orders for new buildings, with the result that, very quickly, the number of ships available is again in excess of demand. It seems, despite the prospects of an increase in the international seaborne trade of LPG in the years to come, that this is happening again and the new century might very well start with an excess of available tonnage.

LPG WORLD FLEET						
Type, Number and Capacity of LPG Carrier Fleet (at end 1997)						
		0-4,999	*5,000-19,999*	*20,000-59,999*	*60,000 101,000*	*Total*
Pressurised	Number of Ships	418	26	0	0	444
	Total Capacity (m³)	752,875	158,626	0	0	911,501
Semi-pressurised	Number of Ships	133	136	7	0	276
	Total Capacity (m³)	389,474	1,217,986	154,452	0	1,761,912
Refrigerated	Number of Ships	14	13	69	90	186
	Total Capacity (m³)	25,792	197,380	2,655,910	6,937,936	9,617,016
Total	Number of Ships	565	175	76	90	906
	Total Capacity (m³)	1,168,141	1,573,992	2,810,362	6,937,936	12,490,431

Table 4.2 Type, Number and Capacity of LPG Tanker Fleet. (Clarkson.)

LPG WORLD FLEET						
Type, Number and Capacity of LPG Carrier on Order (at end 1997)						
		0-4,999	*5,000-19,999*	*20,000-59,999*	*60,000 101,000*	*Total*
Pressurised	Number of Ships	16	0	0	0	16
	Total Capacity (m³)	48,218	0	0	0	48,218
Semi-pressurised	Number of Ships	6	21	7	0	34
	Total Capacity (m³)	26,738	281,280	216,900	0	5,249,18
Refrigerated	Number of Ships	0	0	2	4	6
	Total Capacity (m³)	0	0	99,760	305,000	404,760
Total	Number of Ships	22	21	9	4	56
	Total Capacity (m³)	74,956	281,280	316,660	305,000	977,896

Table 4.3 Type, Number and Capacity of LPG Tankers on Order. (Clarkson.)

27. Semi Pressurised LPG Tanker. (The Author.)

28. Fully Refrigerated LPG Tanker. (The Author.)

4.1.2   THE TRADE

a) *General* – Liquefied gas carriers transport three main cargoes: liquefied petroleum gas (LPG), ammonia and petrochemical gases, each group having its own shipping needs.

The LPG market features large cargo exports from the Arabian Gulf and an active small cargo trade in the North Sea. Ammonia is transported mainly from the Black Sea to the Mediterranean, and from the Arabian Gulf. The trade in petrochemical gases is more varied. At the time of writing, butadiene is moving from North-West Europe and the Mediterranean to the US Gulf, ethylene from the Mediterranean to India, propylene from South America and the US Gulf to North-West Europe and VCM from Japan, Venezuela and the US Gulf to the Far East.

There are more vessels employed on either annual contract of affreightment or time charter than on the spot market.

The demand for vessels is determined by the sea-borne trade in the three groups of cargoes mentioned above and by the distance over which these cargoes are transported.

One of the more interesting characteristics of the liquefied gas trade has always been its volatility. This certainly presents a constant challenge to ship-owners, brokers and traders. Despite this, the overall long-term trend, since the beginning of the trade, has been growth. But the short-term has, in general, been an alternation of short, very healthy bursts with gloom in between.

b) *Liquefied Petroleum Gas (LPG)* – In 1996, the world production of LPG was 165.5 million tonnes and world consumption was 166 million tonnes. This was almost 23% higher than in 1990 and over the last 5 years the increase has been 4.4% per year.

The United States is the largest producer in the world with 35.7 million tonnes and also the largest consumer with 46.5 million tonnes.

Japan is second only to the USA in terms of national consumption. Consumption in 1997 stood at 20.5 million tonnes. Contrary to North America and Western Europe, Japan has to import the bulk of its LPG requirements. This makes Japan the largest importer of LPG in the world, with 15.5 million tonnes of sea-borne delivery in 1997. Imports grew at an average rate of just 0.8% per annum from 1990-1997. Imports to Japan are mainly from the Middle East, Indonesia, Australia and now Malaysia.

South Korea's consumption of LPG has increased by an average of 11.4% per year over the past seven years and in 1997 it reached 7 million tonnes. However, the largest part of its requirement must also be imported and South Korea is the second largest importer of LPG, with 4.5 million tonnes of sea-borne trade in 1997. More than 95% of the LPG imported by South Korea comes from the Middle East.

The demand for LPG in China has increased by almost 23% per year since 1990 and, despite the impressive growth in domestic production, China is the third largest importer of LPG, with a sea-borne trade reaching 3.5 million tonnes before settling at 2.3 million tonnes in 1997. A number of new receiving terminals are already in service or will be commissioned before the end of 2000. China imports LPG mostly from the Middle East and South-East Asia.

Brazil consumes 6.1 million tonnes of LPG per year and demand has grown by 5% per annum over the last five years. Brazil had to import up to 2.5 million tonnes of LPG per year but that was reduced to 2.1 million tonnes in 1997 due to an increase in domestic production. This makes Brazil the fourth largest importer of LPG. Most of the imports come from the Middle East but the amount coming from South America, Africa and the United States is steadily increasing. The quantity of sea-borne trade might be reduced in future, due to the increased availability of products in Argentina, which can be exported overland to Brazil.

LPG consumption in Western Europe was close to 29 million tonnes in 1997 and has increased by 1.6% per annum since 1990. Production, however, has increased much faster, by 4.6% per annum, and stands at 26.4 million tonnes in 1997. European countries imported 13.5 million tonnes of LPG in 1997, of which 9 million tonnes were from EU countries. During the same period, 11.5 million tonnes of LPG were exported from Europe. Much of these imports and exports were intra-regional trade, transported overland. Sea-borne trade came mainly from North Africa and the Middle East and reached a total of almost 4 million tonnes. Turkey alone absorbed close to 1.6 million tonnes.

The United States produced 36 million tonnes and consumed 46.5 million tonnes of LPG in 1997 and both these figures are the largest in the world. However USA is relatively unimportant in terms of international sea-borne trade as most

exchanges are intra-regional and overland. The amount of LPG imported by sea was 1.4 million tonnes in 1997, coming from Africa, the Middle East, Europe and Latin America.

Other Far Eastern countries, such as Taiwan and India, saw their LPG imports increase substantially over the last 7 years, particularly India. In 1997, the amount of sea-borne trade to Taiwan was 0.7 million tonnes, coming mainly from the Middle East, whilst India received 1.1 million tonnes coming from the Middle East and other South East Asia producers, such as Indonesia and Malaysia.

The main LPG exporting areas are: the Middle Eastern countries: 26 million tonnes; Western Europe: 12 million tonnes, mainly transported overland; North America: 6 million tonnes, also mainly transported overland; Asia: 4.6 million tonnes; Africa: 4.5 million tonnes; Latin America: 2.7 million tonnes and Australia: 1.2 million tonnes.

Table 4.4 shows the main international sea-borne trade in LPG in 1997. LPG generates 80% of liquefied gas carrier demand with a total international sea-borne trade of 41 million tonnes in 1997.

LPG - Main Sea-borne Trade - 1997 (million tonnes)							
Imports	*Exports*						
	Middle East	*Africa*	*North Sea*	*S. & C. America*	*Far East*	*Others*	*Total*
Japan	12.3	0.0	0.0	0.0	3.2	0.0	15.5
OECD/Europe	1.0	2.6	0.9	0.0	0.0	0.0	4.5
USA	0.7	0.3	0.0	0.4	0.0	0.0	1.4
S. America	2.5	0.2	0.0	0.0	0.0	0.4	3.1
Far East	8.3	0.0	0.0	0.0	0.6	0.1	9.0
Others	1.2	1.4	0.0	2.3	0.8	1.8	7.5
Total	26.0	4.5	0.9	2.7	4.6	2.3	41.0

Table 4.4 LPG – Main Seaborne Trade – 1997. (Drewry.)

LPG world-wide production is expected to reach 195 million tonnes per annum by the year 2000 if the long-term average growth of 4.1% per year is sustained. Thereafter the growth rate might drop to 3.5% per annum.

International trade in LPG should rise to roughly 65 million tonnes per annum in 2000 and 80 million tonnes per annum in 2005 (Drewry)

c) *Ammonia* – World-wide ammonia production is currently estimated at 120 million tonnes per annum and has barely increased since 1990. Asia is the largest producer with a total output approaching 50 million tonnes of which 26 million tonnes come from China. China has increased its output by 10 million tonnes since 1990. North America has the second largest production with an output of 20 million tonnes which has increased by two million tonnes since 1990. The output from the ex-Soviet Union countries slumped from 22 million tonnes in 1990 to 14 million tonnes in 1994 but has now recovered to 16 million tonnes. Western European production has been reduced from 15 million tonnes in 1990 to 13 million tonnes at present. Other producing regions are Eastern

Europe, Latin America, the Middle East, Africa and Australasia.

The main exporters are the former Soviet Union, followed by Latin America and the Middle East. Many countries are involved in both the import and export of ammonia and this makes it difficult to differentiate between the actual and apparent level of trade. The main importers of ammonia are, again, the former Soviet Union and Eastern Europe, Latin America, Western Europe, the Middle East, North America followed by Asia, Africa and Australasia.

Table 4.5 shows the main movements of ammonia by sea in 1997. Ammonia generated 11% of the liquefied gas carrier demand, with a total international sea-borne trade of almost 12 million tonnes in 1997.

The forecast is for a slow increase of international trade in ammonia reaching about 13.5 million tonnes in 2002.

d) *Petrochemical Gases* – The international sea-borne trade in the main petrochemical gases, accounts for about 9% of the LPG carrier availability and amounted to a total of

Ammonia - Main Sea-borne Trade - 1997 (million tonnes)							
Imports	*Exports*						
	W. Europe	*South America*	*North America*	*Middle East*	*E. Europel FSU*	*Others*	*Total*
Australasia	0.00	0.00	0.00	0.03	0.00	0.06	0.09
Middle East	0.00	0.00	0.00	0.18	0.00	0.00	0.18
South America	0.11	0.17	0.04	0.03	0.00	0.00	0.35
Africa	0.55	0.04	0.00	0.00	0.46	0.12	1.17
Asia	0.30	0.00	0.40	0.88	0.00	0.36	1.94
North America	0.14	1.86	1.15	0.04	0.95	0.20	4.34
Europe	0.54	0.10	0.00	0.03	3.05	0.15	3.87
Total	1.64	2.17	1.59	1.19	4.46	0.89	11.93

Table 4.5 Ammonia – Main Seaborne Trade – 1997. (Drewry.)

5.86 million tonnes in 1995. Table 4.6 shows the main international sea-borne movement of petrochemical gases in 1995. These figures include ethylene, propylene, butadiene and VCM.

i) Ethylene – The total world production of ethylene in 1996 was 75.77 million tonnes, which was 87% of the total world production capacity. Ethylene production grew by an average of 5% between 1990 and 1996. The main producing countries are: North America: 25.2 million tonnes; Western Europe: 17.78 million tonnes; almost equalled by the Far East: 17.65 million tonnes; the Middle East and Africa: 5.64 million tonnes; Eastern Europe and the former Soviet Union: 4.99 million tonnes and Latin America: 4.52 million tonnes.

Petrochemical Gases - Main Sea-borne Trade - 1995 (million tonnes)									
Imports	*Exports*								
	Europe	*North America*	*Japan*	*Africa*	*Middle East*	*South America*	*Far East*	*Others*	*Total*
Others	0.06	0.05	0.01	0.00	0.01	0.01	0.00	0.00	0.14
N. America	0.30	0.00	0.01	0.00	0.07	0.03	0.03	0.00	0.44
S. America	0.06	0.27	0.00	0.00	0.00	0.00	0.00	0.00	0.33
Far East	0.24	0.49	0.75	0.05	0.45	0.13	0.70	0.05	2.86
Europe	1.70	0.03	0.02	0.14	0.03	0.01	0.02	0.14	2.09
Total	2.36	0.84	0.79	0.19	0.56	0.18	0.75	0.19	5.86

Table 4.6 Petrochemical Gases – Main Seaborne Trade – 1995. (Drewry.)

29. Fully Refrigerated LPG Tanker. (The Author.)

The main exporters are Western Europe: 2.3 million tonnes; South Korea: 0.3 million tonnes; Japan: 0.2 million tonnes and the USA.

The main importers are Western Europe: 1.948 million tonnes; India: 0.327 million tonnes; Taiwan: 0.186 million tonnes, then Thailand, Indonesia, Japan, South Korea and the USA.

Total world production of ethylene is forecast to increase by 4.8% per year up to 95 million tonnes by 2002, but due to the development of domestic production in the main user countries, the prospects for growth in the international sea-borne trade in the coming years are not good.

ii) Propylene – The total world production of propylene has increased from 20 million tonnes in 1990 to almost 42 million tonnes in 1996, due to strong demand for polypropylene. Propylene trade is influenced by the fact that there is excess production in the USA, Japan, South Korea, Italy and Libya and import demand in, for example, South East Asia.

The main exporting countries are Western Europe: 2.176 million tonnes; USA: 0.286 million tonnes; South Korea: 0.235 million tonnes and Japan: 0.219 million tonnes. The main importing countries are Western Europe: 1.865 million tonnes; Taiwan: 0.261 million tonnes; Mexico: 0.193 million tonnes; South Korea: 0.115 million tonnes, and Thailand, USA, China and Japan.

Propylene demand is forecast to grow by 5.6% per year up to 50 million tonnes in 2000. Serious propylene deficits are forecast for Europe and Asia which will be met by the USA and the Middle East. Contrary to ethylene, the prospects for long haul propylene trade in the near future are likely to improve.

iii) Butadiene – World production of butadiene stands at 6.7 million tonnes in 1996 and it is expected to increase by 4.2% per annum in the coming years to reach 8.5 million tonnes in 2001.

The main countries exporting butadiene are Europe: 0.86 million tonnes; South Korea: 0.190 million tonnes and Japan: 0.075 million tonnes. The main countries importing butadiene are Europe: 0.493 million tonnes; the USA: 0.361 million tonnes; Taiwan: 0.195 million tonnes and China: 0.044 million tonnes. The total volume of international sea-borne trade in 1996 was approximately 0.8 million tonnes per annum.

iv) Vinyl Chloride Monomer (VCM) – World production of VCM was 23.3 million tonnes in 1996 and is expected to increase to 27.3 million tonnes in 2000. The USA has long been the world's largest VCM exporter, mainly to the Far East and South East Asia. However, in recent years, Japan has gradually replaced the USA as supplier to the Asia-Pacific region. Taiwan used to be the largest importer of VCM, but the rapid development of its own domestic production has reduced its imports from 0.27 million tonnes in 1994 to less than 0.13 million tonnes in 1996. South Korea is now the largest importer of VCM, taking more than 0.3 million tonnes in 1996.

In 1996, the main VCM exporting countries were the USA: 0.982 million tonnes; Japan: 0.315 million tonnes and Europe: 0.293 million tonnes. The main importing countries were Europe: 0.869 million tonnes; South Korea: 0.3 million tonnes; the rest of the Asia-Pacific region: 0.397 million tonnes and Latin America: 0.430 million tonnes.

Most of the increases in VCM production are forecast to take place in South East Asia and North America. This will considerably reduce the need for imports in South East Asia and the prospects for growth in international sea-borne trade of VCM in the coming years look poor, especially for long-haul trades.

4.1.3 THE TERMINALS

There are almost 100 exporting terminals and 180 importing terminals handling LPG and petrochemical gases around the world. This number does not exactly reflect the total number of LPG terminals, as some are dual purpose, exporting and importing at the same time. They vary greatly in the volume of storage available and in the size of ship which can be accommodated.

In the same way as the ships, terminals can easily be designed to handle all types of liquefied gases. Different types and levels of safety equipment would be installed depending on the products handled. The product to be handled by any given terminal will obviously depend on what is available in that particular area. Some large and very sophisticated terminals in Western Europe can load or discharge many different products at one time. Some other terminals, although equipped with large storage tanks, are only designed to handle the one type of product available in their geographic area.

Many terminals are only equipped with pressurised tanks and can only receive small, pressurised ships. This is why there are so many of these ships, mostly involved in domestic or regional trade. The large, fully-refrigerated terminals are to be found mainly in Japan, Korea, Taiwan, United States, Europe and Australasia for importing terminals and the Far East, the Middle East, North Africa, Australasia, Europe and United States for exporting terminals.

Ship-to-ship transfer has been extensively used in the LPG trade for delivering cargoes, either when no suitable terminal was available or when it was found more economical to use large ships discharging onto small ships, able to deliver the product to limited shore facilities. In some cases, such as in China in recent years, large ships were anchored off-shore, serving as floating storage pending the construction of shore tanks or

because this was found a more economical means of delivery. The storage ships were supplied by visiting ships, bringing the product from the exporter and they then discharged into a fleet of smaller, usually pressurised, ships.

A trend developed over recent years is to use a modified ship or some purpose-built structure as floating storage on an offshore LPG production site. The floating storage receives the LPG, either propane or butane or a mixture of both, directly from the well or from a floating production platform. Visiting ships load from the floating storage and transport the product to its final destination. Several of these units are now in operation, mainly in Africa and the Far East.

4.1.4 COMMERCIAL TITLES

LPG is sold on the international market in several different ways:

- Large quantities are sold under medium-term contracts by producing companies, as, for example Saudi Aramco or Sonatrach, to large users, such as the utility companies or petrochemical complexes, in Japan, or Europe or to large traders.

- Some quantities are sold, mostly on a spot basis, by the same large producers and other smaller producers to smaller users and distributors.

- Some quantities are sold by traders to small users.

The price of LPG varies substantially between summer-time, when demand is not so heavy and winter-time when demand increases, particularly if the winter is severe. It is obvious that producers and traders who are able to store LPG during the low-price seasons are able to make a considerable profit when selling during high-price seasons. This makes for an active spot market in periods of high demand. However, this can be risky as, if the winter temperatures remain high, prices will remain low and the opportunity for profit will slip away.

Among the petrochemical gases, ammonia is traded broadly along the same lines as LPG. Large quantities of ammonia are sold under medium-term contracts by producing companies to users, who are mainly urea producers. Some quantities are also sold by traders taking advantage of the market fluctuations. Finally, there are always some small quantities sold on a spot basis to compensate for unexpected shortages, due either to failed delivery or increased demand.

Other petrochemical gases, such as ethylene, propylene, butadiene and vinyl chloride monomer, are sold mostly by refineries, directly to users, under medium-term contracts. However, there is always a demand for small quantities to be sold on a spot basis.

In both cases, medium-term contract or spot sales, a transportation contract has to be signed with the ship-owner. This is always in the form of a time-charter, which is essentially an operating lease. The only exception to this is when the ship-owner is also a trader and transports his own product.

A time-charter specifies the main characteristics of the vessel, the obligations of the ship-owner and of the charterer. LPG time-charters are based on conventional oil tanker charter provisions, with additional clauses relating to the specific products to be transported.

30. LPG Terminal. (SIGTTO.)

41

Hire charges are normally paid throughout the charter period, except when the ship is not available due to some failure of ship or owner. Hire is paid monthly in advance based on an all-inclusive daily rate applicable to the entire period. The ship-owner pays for all the operating costs of the vessel, except for fuel, port charges and canal dues (Suez and Panama), which are the responsibility of the charterer. In some very exceptional cases, for example, if the charterer should order the vessel to sail into a war zone where an insurance premium is required, this is also the responsibility of the charterer.

Special clauses applicable to LPG charters relate to the specification of the cargo to be loaded, the conditions of the cargo in terms of quality, pressure and temperature at loading and at discharge and the provisions for measuring the cargo quantity on board.

LPG and petrochemical gases are sold based on their weight and the quantity loaded and discharged is, most of the time, measured on board and calculated under the supervision of an independent surveyor.

The master signs a bill of lading, which confirms ownership of the cargo and allows the receiver to accept the cargo at the discharging port. A copy of the bill of lading is usually retained on board.

4.2 LIQUEFIED NATURAL GAS (LNG)

4.2.1 THE FLEET

The development of LNG shipping has been more rapid than that of LPG shipping. The total capacity of LNG ships equalled that of the LPG fleet by the mid-80's after being in existence half as long and with one-tenth the number of ships.

The first LNG ships were of relatively small capacity, between 20,000 and 30,000 m^3. At the end of the 60's, sizes over 70,000 m^3 were already used. Polar Alaska and Arctic Tokyo, delivered in 1969/70, had a capacity of 71,500 m^3. Very soon after that, the first 125,000 m^3 capacity ships were built. This size (i.e. 125,000-130,000 m^3) has been a standard for many years and has only been slightly increased on the most recent ships with capacities up to 138,000 m^3. Ships have recently been discussed with capacities of 145,000 m^3. All shipyards have designs of ships with capacities up to 160,000 m^3 or even 200,000 m^3, and even larger ships would probably be feasible. Up to now, however, there has not been much interest for larger sizes.

There are several reasons for the consistency in size:

- Most existing terminals were built to accommodate ships in the 125,000/135,000 m^3 range and, were new terminals to be designed and built for larger ships, they would not be able to accommodate smaller ships and would lose flexibility.

- Large volume projects favour reliability over profitability by preferring two smaller ships rather than one very large vessel.

- Shipyards have been developing equipment to build standard size ships and more investment would be needed if the size was substantially changed.

The number of LNG ships in January 2000 is 117, with another 16 on order. Three-quarters of the existing ships and 95% of the ships on order are of a capacity larger than 125,000 m^3. Chart 4.2 and table 4.7 show the progression of the LNG Fleet through the years and table 4.8 shows the situation at the end of 1998. Table 4.9 shows the number of ships on order at the end of 1999.

LNG World Fleet						
Type, Number and Capacity of LNG Carrier Fleet (at end 1999)						
		0-19,999	**20,000-59,999**	**60,000-99,999**	**100,000 140,000**	**Total**
Membrane	*Number of Ships*	3	5	11	29	48
	Total Capacity (m³)	56,781	201,931	803,400	3,764,181	4,826,293
Self-supporting	*Number of Ships*	1	6	4	58	69
	Total Capacity (m³)	19,474	206,476	354,960	10,768,606	11,349,516
Total	*Number of Ships*	4	11	15	87	117
	Total Capacity (m³)	76,255	408,407	1,158,360	14,532,787	16,175,809

Table 4.7 Type, Number and Capacity of LNG Tanker Fleet. (Clarkson.)

	Number of Ships	**Total Capacity (1000 m³)**
1970	5	22
1980	52	5,437
1990	64	6,991
1999	117	16,176

Table 4.8 LNG Tankers – Growth of World Fleet to End of 1999. (Clarkson.)

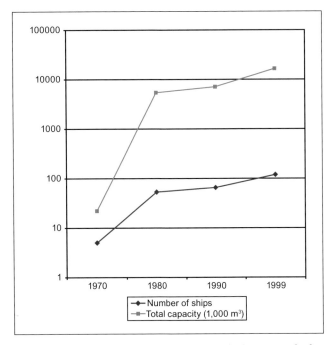

Chart 4.2 LNG Tankers – Growth of World Fleet to End of 1999.

LNG World Fleet						
Type, Number and Capacity of LNG Carriers on order (at end 1999)						
		0-19,999	*20,000-59,999*	*60,000-99,999*	*100,000 140,000*	*Total*
Membrane	*Number of Ships*	1	0	1	7	8
	Total Capacity (m³)	22,500	0	0	964,400	986,900
Self-supporting	*Number of Ships*	0	0	0	8	8
	Total Capacity (m³)	0	0	0	1,100,000	1,100,000
Total	*Number of Ships*	1	0	1	15	16
	Total Capacity (m³)	22,500	0	0	2,064,400	2,086,900

Table 4.9 Type, Number and Capacity of LNG Tankers on Order at End of 1999. (Clarkson.)

4.2.2 THE TRADE

83 million tonnes of LNG were carried by ship during 1998. More than 50% of the total quantity was delivered to Japan from countries as diverse as USA, Australia, Indonesia, Malaysia, Brunei, Abu Dhabi and Qatar.

Most of this LNG is sold under long term contracts and the ships transporting it are chartered for periods of 20 or even 25 years.

LNG projects are very complicated to organise. The investment required is huge, in the order of several billion US Dollars. To obtain the required finance, the volume of product contracted, the duration of the contract and the commercial security of the project have to satisfy the lenders that the return on their investment is reasonably safe for the duration of the contract.

The development of an LNG project up to delivery of the first cargo would include:

- Discovery of the gas and confirmation that reserves are sufficient for the intended project.

- Negotiation of a sale and purchase contract to be signed between the supplier and the buyer which includes, amongst other things, the quantity to be delivered, the purchase price, the starting date and duration of the contract and provisions to protect both parties in case of interruption.

- Development drilling of the non-associated gas field or separation of gas and oil production in an associated gas field.

- Construction of the necessary pipeline and compressors to deliver gas to the liquefaction plant.

- Construction of the liquefaction plant and LNG storage tanks.

- Construction of LNG loading lines and facilities, ship berth and sometimes harbour works such as breakwaters and dredging.

- LNG ship construction or acquisition of existing vessels.

- Construction of LNG discharging berth, unloading lines and facilities and sometimes harbour works.

- Construction of LNG receiving terminal including storage, vaporisation and send-out facilities.

- Tie-in to a gas distribution network or electrical power plant.

All these facilities, which constitute what is called the LNG chain, have to be negotiated, financed, designed and built in due time to be available for the start-up of the project.

All this involves different countries, different contractors, shipyards, suppliers of large units of equipment, banks, insurance companies, lawyers and more. It is not surprising that, from the initial discovery of the gas to the first delivery of cargo, a period of five years seems to be the minimum time required.

Most LNG contracts are signed for periods of 20, sometimes 25 years and the necessary guarantees to protect all partners in the project during these long periods are developed only after extensive and delicate negotiations. The commercial and legal aspects of the total LNG project have proved to be the most time consuming and frustrating. Several projects have aborted at a very advanced stage, during such negotiations. The most spectacular case was the termination of the very large El Paso project between Algeria and the USA at the beginning of the 1980's after ten years preparation and only two years of operation.

At the end of 1998, 44 long-term LNG contracts were operating, involving 23 country-to-country trades. The LNG was loaded at 14 loading terminals and discharged at 32 receiving terminals. Table 4.10 shows the main international sea-borne trades of LNG in 1998.

Several new contracts started operating during 1998 and 1999. These include deliveries from Qatar to Japan, Algeria to Greece, Nigeria to Europe and Trinidad and Tobago to the USA and Europe.

A number of other projects are being discussed, with starting dates expected within the next two to three years. These involve new liquefaction plants or expansions being built, such as in Qatar, Australia, Malaysia, Oman, Yemen and in the Sakhalin Islands and new reception facilities, as in several places in India, Puerto Rico, China, Korea and Taiwan. Some of these projects are more secure than others. The recent economical slow down in the Far-Eastern countries has delayed a few projects. The attraction of LNG as a clean fuel, however, added to efforts to reduce its price, aided by the very strong competition existing between sellers, is maintaining good prospects of a regular increase in the quantity of LNG sold around the world.

LNG - Main Seaborne Trade - 1998 (million tonnes)										
Imports	*Exports*									
	Indonesia	*Algeria*	*Malaysia*	*Brunei*	*Australia*	*Abu-Dhabi*	*Libya*	*USA*	*Qatar*	*Total*
USA	0.00	1.40	0.00	0.00	0.20	0.05	0.00	0.00	0.00	1.65
Taiwan	1.60	0.00	1.60	0.00	0.00	0.00	0.00	0.00	0.00	3.20
S. Korea	6.80	0.00	4.00	0.70	0.00	0.00	0.00	0.00	0.00	11.50
OECD	0.00	16.40	0.00	0.00	0.00	0.90	0.80	0.00	0.10	18.20
Japan	18.00	0.00	9.30	5.30	6.90	4.50	0.00	1.30	2.00	47.30
Total	26.40	17.80	14.90	6.00	7.10	5.45	0.80	1.30	2.10	81.85

Table 4.10 LNG – Main Seaborne Trade – 1998. (GIIGNL.)

31. LNG Tanker of the Gaz Transport Membrane Type. (The Author.)

In addition to long-term contracts, approximately 5 million tonnes of LNG have been traded on short-term contracts during 1998, with ships hired on short-term or even voyage charter. Many liquefaction plants are able to produce slightly more than their contractual obligations and several vessels are still available for short-term charter. Some buyers require small quantities, pending the start of a long-term contract or to supplement existing delivered quantities. These factors have led to the development of short-term contracts. Short-term LNG trades have taken place between Abu Dhabi and Europe or the USA, between Australia and Europe, between Brunei, Malaysia, Indonesia, Australia and Japan, Taiwan, Korea, between Australia and the USA, and more recently between Malaysia and the USA, a distance of 12,700 miles, setting a record for the longest haul for a cargo of LNG.

It would seem that more short-term contracts will be developed in the future, although ship availability might be a restricting factor.

4.2.3 THE TERMINALS

We have seen above that there are, at present, 14 LNG loading terminals and 32 LNG receiving terminals around the world. All, bar 2 loading and 7 receiving terminals, have berths designed for ships of 125,000 m³ or above. Some of these berths can also receive smaller ships. All the loading and receiving berths, except for 2, have been specially built and are only used to receive LNG vessels. The two exceptions are berths in Japan which were converted from oil tanker berths.

Some terminals have only one berth, but others, designed to deliver or receive larger quantities, can have up to three or four different berths, enabling them to serve several ships at the same time.

32. LNG Loading Terminal with Ship.

33. LNG Receiving Terminal. (Kansai Electric.)

In the near future, several new loading terminals will start operation in Trinidad and Tobago, Nigeria, Oman and Yemen as well as two receiving terminals in Greece and Puerto Rico, and several others are being discussed, in particular in India and also Korea, China and Taiwan.

Although some efforts have been made to achieve some sort of standardisation of berth design, this has only been effective in determining the position and diameter of the loading/discharging manifolds and the position of the hooks for mooring lines. Ships calling at several different berths must have other equipment adapted to each berth. This applies mainly to the location of the shore gangway and the connections and type of systems used for communications and Emergency Shut-Down System (ESDS).

The design of an LNG terminal involves more than the design of the berth itself. Access from the sea and services provided by the ports to ensure the ships a safe transit in and out of port are also very important, as well as the availability of safety equipment, trained personnel and well specified and rehearsed contingency procedures in case of accident.

4.2.4 COMMERCIAL TITLES

Liquefied Natural Gas (LNG) is usually sold under long-term contracts, signed for periods of 15 to 25 years. The most common contract duration is 20 years. There are good reasons for signing contracts for such long periods.

- LNG requires very extensive facilities for its production as well as for its use.

- The establishment of an LNG project requires huge investments which are only possible if a reasonable return is guaranteed over a period sufficient at least to recover the value of the investment.

- An interruption of the LNG supply would affect large numbers of people who would be deprived of their domestic gas or electricity supply.

With the exception of the USA and Australia, LNG tends to be produced in developing countries, and used in developed countries. However, this trend is changing with the soon-to-be started import projects in India and China.

Sellers of LNG are usually groups of various organisations. These can include the oil company who discovered the gas, the government of the country where the gas is located, banks and finance organisations funding the project, and, possibly, following a recent trend, representatives of the buyers, interested in securing their supply.

Buyers of LNG are, very often, the large utility companies able to build and manage the necessary infrastructure to receive, distribute or otherwise use the gas.

At the start of negotiations between buyers and sellers, a Letter Of Intent (LOI), containing few details and not considered binding, is usually signed. This is followed by the lengthy negotiation of the final Sale and Purchase Agreement (SPA). However, there is often an intermediate stage, which is marked by the signature of a Memorandum of Understanding (MOU), sometimes called Heads of Agreement (HOA). This document has a limited life, but includes all the key commercial terms, including the LNG price and provides a much higher level of commitment between the parties than the Letter of Intent. In some recent negotiations, a Confirmation of Intent (COI) has been used. A COI is a firmer, more defined version of the industry standard LOI. The COI defines volume and build-up, as well as establishing a price range within which the final sales price will be agreed. The COI is not a legally binding document.

However, the firm character of the COI allows sellers and buyers to move directly to a SPA, avoiding the intermediate step of negotiating a MOU. The period between signature of the LOI and the final signature of the SPA can be very long, sometimes one year or more. During this time, the partners must arrange the financing necessary to carry out the project.

The Sales Contract can be Free on Board (FOB) if the buyer is providing the shipping, or Cost Insurance and Freight (CIF) or Ex-Ship if the seller provides the shipping. In the first case, title in the cargo is transferred to the buyer when the cargo crosses the rail of the ship at the loading port. In the second case, title only transfers when the cargo crosses the rail of the ship at the discharging port. The type of contract signed determines which party has the responsibility to provide the shipping for transporting the cargo between the loading and discharging port.

Either way, a transportation contract must be signed with the shipowner, normally in the form of a Time Charter or of a Contract of Affreightment (COA), which are both essentially operating leases. The Time Charter includes the rate of hire for the use of the vessel and payment of the operating costs, which cover all costs required for the ship's operation, except fuel, LN2, port charges and canal dues (Suez and Panama). These items, referred to as voyage costs, are the responsibility of the charterer. In case of a COA, the remuneration is based on the quantity of cargo transported and includes all operating and voyage costs.

The hire is paid monthly in advance for short-term charters of up to 3 years, based on an all-inclusive daily rate which applies for the entire period. For longer-term charters, the hire is divided into the Capital Element, which remains fixed, usually for the full term of the charter, and the Operating Element which depends on the actual cost of ship operation and takes into account cost escalation.

Hire charges are normally paid throughout the charter period, except when the ship is not available due to some failure of vessel or owner. For long-term charters, the scheduled dry docking periods are also designated off-hire.

A time-charter specifies the main characteristics of the ship, the obligations of the ship owner and of the charterer. LNG time-charters are similar to LPG time-charters and are based on conventional oil tanker charter provisions, with additional clauses relating to cryogenic performance. These additional clauses are quite different in an LNG charter-party from those in an LPG contract. One clause specific to LNG time-charters relates to the use of the cargo boil-off as fuel. The fuel consumption and the amount of boil-off generated, paid for by the charterer, are influenced by the way the ship is operated and maintained, which is the responsibility of the ship operator. The conversion of the heating value of boil-off gas to its fuel-oil equivalent can lead to serious discussions during charter-party negotiations, when it comes to the determination of possible penalties for exceeding the agreed values.

Another important clause of an LNG charter-party is the specification for measurement of cargo quantity on board. The volume of cargo sold is always measured on board ship. This is the volume of cargo loaded at the loading port in the case of an FOB contract and the volume of cargo discharged at the receiving port in the case of a CIF or Ex-Ship contract. All LNG ships have their tanks very carefully measured by an accredited independent surveyor and these measurements are, very often, certified by the customs authorities of the seller's and buyer's countries. The measurement equipment in the tanks, which includes level, pressure and temperature gauges, are also very carefully checked and regularly calibrated under third-party supervision. Modern ships are all equipped with computerised custody transfer systems, which automatically calculate the volume of product in the tanks with all necessary corrections for ship trim and list and cargo temperature. Such calculations are always confirmed by an accredited, independent surveyor.

LPG and other petrochemical gases are manufactured products based on well-defined specifications. Their composition is well known and they are sold by weight. LNG, on the contrary, is a natural product of variable composition, which can contain significant amounts of nitrogen which has no commercial value. This is why the LNG unit of sale is based on calorific value expressed in million BTU per unit of volume.

One way of determining the calorific value of a product is to know its exact chemical composition. The chemical composition of the LNG cargo delivered is determined by chromatographic analysis of samples taken at random during the loading or discharging operation. The volume of cargo loaded or discharged, as measured on board, and the calorific value determined by the chromatographic analysis are used to produce the invoice representing the value of the cargo delivered.

The original of the bill of lading is sent to the buyer's representative at the receiving port and a copy is carried on board.

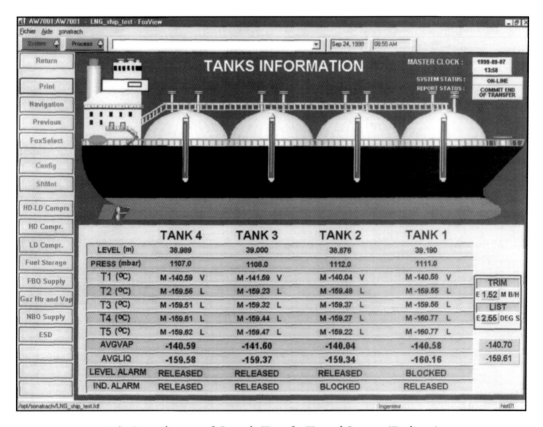

34. Reproduction of Custody Transfer Typical Screen. (Foxboro.)

35. LNG Tanker with Hard Arms Connected. (SIGTTO.)

Chapter 5
VARIOUS TYPES OF LIQUEFIED GAS TANKERS

5.1 GENERAL – THE IMO CODE DEFINITIONS

The evolution of liquefied gas tankers over the years has been broadly determined by the different types of product to be transported, their physical condition at the loading and discharging ports and the improvement of technology. We have seen that the first ships were designed to transport small quantities of butane and propane at ambient temperature. The maximum pressure of propane at +45°C* is 16 bar gauge and this decided the maximum pressure for which the tanks had to be designed. Very soon, ammonia was added to the list of products to be transported and the maximum pressure to be considered for the design of the cargo tanks was increased to 18 bar gauge, as this is the maximum pressure of ammonia at +45°C*. The technology and materials available for the construction of the tanks at that time only allowed fairly small units. The weight of the tanks was a further limitation on ship size.

Demand for the transport of larger volumes of cargo and development of improved reliquefaction and metallurgical technology allowed the construction of tanks with lower maximum design pressures and lower minimum temperatures, e.g. progression to semi-pressurised and fully refrigerated ships and ethylene tankers.

The most recent challenge was the need to transport LNG with a minimum temperature of –162°C, a critical pressure of 82 bar, which precluded any possibility of pressurised or semi-pressurised tanks, and no practical on board means of reliquefaction. The inventiveness of the designers was fully demonstrated by the number of different tank designs to come off the drawing boards.

This was the situation at the end of the 1960's. The liquefied gas tanker fleet was composed of a large number of small pressurised ships, a few semi-pressurised and fully refrigerated ships and some LNG tankers. The safety of the transport of liquefied gas by sea had always raised some concern. Although the general safety record of the fleet was good, a few isolated incidents were attracting public attention. These were due, amongst other causes, to the dubious stability of some of the small pressurised ships and to the practice of carrying liquid petroleum products in the side tanks of fully refrigerated ships. This was the cause of the disastrous fire on board the YoyoMaru in the Tokyo Bay in 1974.

In 1968, the Inter-Governmental Maritime Consultative Organization (IMCO), as it was known at the time, now the International Maritime Organization (IMO), started, a programme to develop standards for vessels carrying hazardous

---

* +45°C is considered the maximum temperature that a cargo is likely to reach during any sea-going voyage. On pressurised ships without a refrigeration system, a network of water pipes with spray nozzles is arranged over the tank tops to cool the tanks if the temperature is likely to rise above this limit.

materials in bulk. The *Code for the Construction of Ships Carrying Dangerous Chemicals in Bulk* was completed in 1971 and adopted as Resolution A.212(VII). The programme was continued and, in November 1975, the *Code for the Construction and Equipment of Ships Carrying Liquefied Gases in Bulk (GC Code)* was adopted by the Ninth Assembly of the IMCO as Resolution A.328(IX).

The Resolution recommended that all member Governments incorporate its contents into national regulations as soon as possible. The purpose of the GC Code is to provide internationally agreed standards of design, construction and operation for the safe carriage of liquefied gas in bulk.

The GC Code was intended to apply only to new ships and it defined the details of its application. Basically, all ships ordered after October 1976 or delivered after June 1980 had to comply fully with the Code.

The situation of Existing Ships, those delivered prior to 1976/1980 period, was covered by a separate *Code for Existing Ships* and the IMCO Assembly, in Resolution A.329 (IX), recommended that ships delivered between those two dates be built, so far as reasonable and practicable, according to the Code for new ships.

The GC Code was supported by all major countries involved in liquefied gas shipping and by all major classification societies and it was adopted very quickly as the only acceptable standard for the design, construction and operation of liquefied gas tankers.

The GC Code regulates the transport of 27 liquefied gases and certain other substances. It defines a liquefied gas as a product having a vapour pressure of 2.8 bar absolute at a temperature of 37.8°C. A few other chemical products such as chlorine or ethylene oxide, which nearly meet the definition of a liquefied gas, were included because they are commonly transported in gas ships.

A revised edition of the GC Code was published in 1993. This edition includes the four sets of amendments introduced since 1975, and converts all measurement units to the SI system. This new edition is called *The IMO International Code for the Construction and Equipment of Ships Carrying Liquefied Gas in Bulk or IGC Code*. [3]

The main thrust of the IGC Code is to focus attention on the design of the cargo containment systems, piping systems, pressure vessels, construction materials, ship survival capability and cargo tank locations in order to minimise the release of cargo in the event of a casualty. These were the areas for which specific details and requirements were most needed. The IGC Code also recognises that, in order to ensure the safe transport of liquefied gases, the total system must be appraised, including other equally important aspects such as operations, traffic control and handling in port. The IGC Code contains detailed requirements governing the complete design and fitting-out of new ships.

Following the application of the GC Code, the various designs of liquefied gas carriers were confirmed as they are known today.

The GC Code defined various types of cargo containment systems, which can be summarised as follows:

- *Integral tanks,* form a structural part of the ship's hull and are influenced in the same manner and by the same loads which stress the adjacent hull structure.

- *Membrane tanks,* non-self supporting tanks which consist of a thin layer (membrane) supported through insulation by the adjacent hull structure. The membrane is designed in such a way that thermal and other expansion or contraction is accommodated without unduly stressing the membrane. This category of tank includes the internal insulation systems.

- *Semi-membrane tanks,* self-supporting when empty; when loaded, the top, bottom and sides must be supported by the adjacent hull structure.

- *Independent tanks,* self-supporting, these do not form part of the ship's hull and are not essential for hull strength. Three categories of independent tanks are considered:

  o *Independent tanks type A* whose primary design follows classic classification society structural analysis procedures.

  o *Independent tanks type B* which are designed using model tests, refined analytical tools and analysis methods to determine stress levels, fatigue life, and crack propagation characteristics.

  o *Independent tanks type C* (also referred to as pressure tanks) which meet pressure vessel criteria where the dominant stress producing load is the service vapour pressure.

36. LNG Tanker of the Gaz Transport Membrane Type. (The Author.)

A design vapour pressure limitation of 0.25 bar is placed on integral tanks, membrane tanks, semi-membrane tanks and independent tanks type A, with special consideration for an increase to 0.7 bar where tank scantlings and insulation are modified as appropriate.

The design vapour pressure limit for independent tanks type B with flat surfaces is limited to 0.7 bar.

The design vapour pressure limit for independent tank type C is calculated according to tank size and material characteristics. Calculation procedures are explained in detail in the GC Code.

Design temperature limitation is only given for integral tanks. The limit of –10°C is based on the concern for thermally induced stresses in the hull girder.

In a number of instances, a secondary barrier, acting as temporary containment for any envisaged leakage of liquid cargo through the primary barrier, must be provided.

Membrane and certain semi-membrane tanks, integral tanks for design temperatures below –10°C and independent tanks type A are required to have a full secondary barrier. Independent type B tanks and certain semi-membrane tanks are only required to have a partial secondary barrier. This is because they are fabricated to higher standards and tolerances and are made of materials that have a proven superior resistance to crack initiation and propagation. Independent tanks type C do not require any secondary barrier.

The hull is permitted to act as a secondary barrier only in the case of cargo temperatures above –55°C.

The GC Code is not limited to establishing standards for the design of the cargo containment system. It also provides standards for other safety systems aimed at minimising the release of cargo

or the effect of such a release in the event of a vessel casualty.

The application of most of these various types of cargo tanks has determined current ship design which will now be reviewed. Certain types, although listed in the Code, have not yet found favour with the designers.

5.2   FULLY PRESSURISED SHIPS

These ships are all equipped with independent tanks type C. The maximum working pressure can be up to 18 bar and the minimum allowed temperature is usually –5°C, although some ships have been designed for temperatures as low as –24°C. The first ships of this type carried their cargo in a number of vertical pressure vessels. Modern pressurised ships can have capacities between 500 and 10,000 m^3 with horizontal cylindrical or spherical shaped tanks.

Cylindrical tanks are arranged below or partly below deck, mounted on cradle-shaped foundations. The tanks are equipped with domes located as far forward as possible, to avoid vapour pockets, where all connections necessary for loading, discharging, sampling and gauging of liquid level, pressure and temperature are located. Domes of tanks located below deck protrude through the deck. The combined loading/discharging pipe is located as far aft and as near to the tank bottom as possible, thus reducing the amount of cargo which remains on board at the end of discharge.

Spherical tanks are supported at their equator by a cylinder resting on the double bottom.

No deepwell or submerged cargo pumps are installed on ships of this type. Discharge is achieved by pumping vapour from another tank with a compressor to increase the tank pressure and push the liquid out. Booster pumps can be installed to speed up the operation.

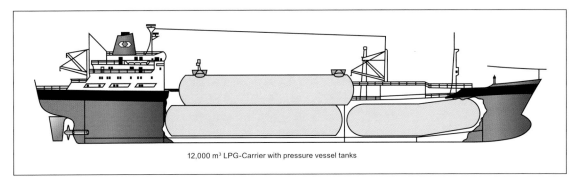

12,000 m³ LPG-Carrier with pressure vessel tanks

37. Drawing of a Pressurised LPG Tanker. (SIGTTO.)

Fully-pressurised ships equipped with type C independent tanks are simple, easy to build and easy to operate. The material used for the cargo tanks and piping can be normal steel and no insulation is necessary, as the cargo is carried at ambient temperature. The cargo requires no maintenance between loading and discharge and no reliquefaction equipment is necessary. The operation is very similar to that of an oil tanker.

On the minus side, the shape of the cargo tanks does not allow an optimum use of the under-deck space and, due to the high maximum working pressure, their weight and, therefore, their cost are high. As tanks increase in diameter, the wall thickness must be correspondingly increased for the same design pressure with the consequence of having to apply expensive stress-relieving procedures. Finally, the cargo quantity transported is lower per weight than for a semi-pressurised or fully refrigerated ship, due to the lower specific gravity of the cargo at ambient temperature. Above a certain tank size, it is more economical to install a refrigeration plant and to maintain a reduced pressure in the tanks.

5.3 SEMI-PRESSURISED SHIPS

These ships are also equipped with independent type C cargo tanks. The maximum working pressure is usually limited to between 5 and 7 bar. Older ships had minimum service temperatures not lower than –5°C, however, more recent ships can carry products with minimum temperature as low as –48°C (or even –105°C for ethylene tankers). The tanks are usually horizontal, cylindrical or bi-lobed, mounted on saddle supports. They are internally stiffened with wash bulkheads and stiffening rings notched top and bottom to allow vapour and liquid flow. To minimise heat flow into the cargo tanks and to protect the ship structure from the effect of low temperatures, a thick layer of insulation is required all around the tanks. The insulation material is usually polyurethane foam or polystyrene, pre-formed or projected, covered by a moisture-tight protection, usually made of aluminium foil. The thickness of the insulation material depends on the minimum temperature at which the cargo is carried. The refrigeration or reliquefaction plant maintains the temperature of the cargo by removing the boil-off vapours from the tank and returning them in liquid form. The tanks usually have two domes to accommodate all piping and instrument connections. The vapour dome, located approximately at the middle of the tank where the vapour line, pressure exhaust valves vent line and level gauges are located and the liquid dome, located on the aft-part of the tank, where the liquid loading line and cargo pump discharge lines are connected. The cargo piping

38. Semi Pressurised LPG Tanker. (SIGTTO.)

39. Semi Pressurised LPG Tanker. (SIGTTO.)

connections are usually equipped with expansion loops or bellows to compensate for movement due to changes in temperature. Deepwell pumps, with the electric motor outside the tank and a long shaft reaching to the bottom, are favored for this type of ship and it is usual to have only one pump installed in each tank. In case of pump failure, the compressors can be used to establish pressure at the top of the tank to push the liquid out.

Booster pumps and cargo heaters are usually installed to allow cargoes to be loaded or discharged at any temperature and transported in a refrigerated condition. A number of different cargoes can be carried simultaneously, even in refrigerated condition and different grades of product can be loaded or discharged at the same time without the possibility of any mixing.

Semi-pressurised ships are more expensive than conventional pressurised ships but their flexibility in service makes them very popular in the trade. As independent tanks type C do not require a secondary barrier, they can even be competitive with the fully refrigerated ships. Current sizes for semi-pressurised ships are between 5,000 and 12,000 m³, but ships as large as 20,000 m³ are currently being built.

Type C tanks with a minimum service temperature equal to or above –50°C are usually built of fine-grained carbon-manganese steel, as recommended by the Code. Tanks for semi-pressurised ethylene tankers, with a minimum service temperature of –105°C, are built of 5% nickel steel or stainless steel.

The advantages of semi-pressurised ships can be summed up as follows:

- Cargo weight to tank weight ratio is 4:1 compared with 2:1 for pressurised ships

- Great flexibility in the conditions accepted for loading and discharging cargoes.

- Higher specific gravity of cargo due to low temperature of transportation increases the quantity loaded for an equal volume.

- Savings due to reduced tank wall thickness are balanced by extra costs due to the need for higher quality materials and reliquefaction equipment.

5.4 FULLY REFRIGERATED SHIPS

These ships are all equipped with prismatic, independent type A tanks, which, according to the Code, require a full secondary barrier. As the cargo temperature is usually limited to –50°C at the lowest, a double hull is not required. A few of the early ships were provided with a double hull extending over the full length of the cargo containment space, the inner hull being of low temperature material and acting as the secondary barrier. The space between the two hulls was used to carry liquid petroleum products. However, after the catastrophic accident of the YoyoMaru in Tokyo Bay, this practice was discontinued. In modern ships, the double hull extends over the bottom bilge area only. The secondary barrier is provided by special steel for the double bottom and bilge chamfer, the side shell and associated structure extending between the bilge chamfer and the bottom of the hopper tanks and the inside plates of the hopper tanks. Transverse bulkheads separate the holds, either single plate or in the form of a cofferdam.

The maximum service pressure of this type of tank is limited to 0.25 bar. The tanks are equipped with a vapour dome in the centre and two liquid domes, one on each side on the aft-part of the tank. The tops of the tanks have inclined chamfers to limit the effects of free surfaces, for stability reasons. The bottoms are rounded to fit the ship's structure in the bilges. A longitudinal bulkhead divides the tanks to limit the effects of sloshing. The tanks rest on a series of wooden supports, isolating the ship structure from their low temperature. Anti-flotation and anti-rolling chocks are installed to prevent the tanks floating off their supports in the event of flooding of the holds and to support the tank sides in case of heavy rolling.

Each tank is equipped with two submerged cargo pumps with the electric motor installed at the bottom of the tank. Some ships are equipped with deepwell pumps, although, for the larger size ships, very long shafts are required. The foot valve at the bottom of the longitudinal bulkhead allows the whole tank to be discharged by only one pump in case of malfunction of one of the pumps.

Independent tanks type A with a minimum service temperature above −50°C are usually built of fine-grained carbon-manganese steel.

The IGC Code recommends specific materials for the construction of cargo tanks. The recommendations are based on the minimum service temperature and also on the compatibility of the material with the cargo to be transported. The IGC Code specifies lower service limits for different grades of material depending on the evaluation of all factors affecting the safe use of this material, including fatigue, stress, thickness and quality of welding. Steel suppliers put their products through special approval testing procedures throughout the manufacturing

40. Fully Refrigerated LPG Tanker. (The Author.)

process. Welding is also an important part of the tank construction and the filler material used is the object of very accurate specification. Welding joints are very carefully checked for default by non-destructive methods. The extent of these checks is also specified in detail.

5.5   INSULATED SHIPS FOR LNG

These ships currently use insulated tanks of either the membrane type or the self-supporting prismatic or spherical type B.

We have seen that earlier ships were fitted with tanks of the self-supporting prismatic type A, in aluminium alloy material, with either a full secondary barrier made of the same material (ESSO type) or a combination of balsa wood and plywood (Conch type). Then the membrane types were built (Gas Transport and Technigaz), followed by the self-supporting spherical type B tanks in 9% nickel steel or aluminium (Kvaerner-Moss) and the prismatic self-supporting type B aluminium tanks (IHI). These are the tanks which, up to now, have been selected for the construction of ships used in commercial ventures. Meanwhile, a large number of other designs were patented, some completely original, others being variations of existing successful ones. A number of these projects were designed in sufficient detail to be proposed for commercial use and a few were even used in the construction of small, prototype vessels.

It would take too long to describe all the designs presented through the years which, in some cases, never got beyond the stage of a nice sketch on a piece of paper. A very comprehensive list can be found in the excellent book "Natural Gas by Sea" written by Roger Ffooks, [20] one of the original designers of LNG containment systems.

It is interesting, however, to list some of the more realistic ideas, to show the level of enthusiasm generated by the prospect of discovering a successful containment design to be used in the construction of LNG ships. This interest still exists and there are, today, groups of designers still trying to create new LNG containment systems which might attract prospective ship-owners.

Many designers tried to emulate, with some variance, the original design of the self-supporting spherical type B tanks by Kvaerner-Moss. The different designs varied only in the shape of the sphere support system, as it is difficult to make one sphere look different from another. The more notable designs came from France, with Gazocean, the US, with Chicago-Bridge, the US and France, with Pittsburgh-Des Moines associated with Gaz Transport, Spain, with Sener and from Japan with Hitachi-Zozen. However, Kvaerner-Moss has, to date, retained the exclusivity of the spherical design for LNG tanks.

The semi-membrane principle attracted many designs, but none were commercially successful. These were from the UK, with Conch and Albiach, France, with Chantiers de l'Atlantique, Germany, with Linde, Spain, with Sener and from Japan, with Bridgestone and IHI.

Another system which attracted the attention of many designers whilst also eluding the expected commercial success was the internal insulation system which would allow the tanks to be constructed in normal steel. Designs came mainly from the US with Rockwell International Wet Wall, Owens Corning Perm-Bar II and Mc Donnell Douglas, who also tried to use the insulation in association with the Gaz Transport membrane system and from Spain with the Metastano Internal Insulation.

Some designers thought that carrying LNG at a higher pressure would have some advantages but this complicated the design by introducing multi-container systems and buyers were not tempted. These systems came from Germany, with the LGA Zellentank, the Linde Curved Wall, the Linde Multi-Vessels, Holland, with the Verolme Vertical Cylindrical and from the USA, with the very high pressure Ocean Transport Pressure System, which eventually evolved into the much lower pressure Ocean Phoenix Transport.

Some other designs were resolutely original in their concept, such as the McMullen double-wall system or the Dytam Concrete LNG Design. However, they were equally unsuccessful.

41. LNG Tanker of the Spherical Tank Type- (Mitsui.)

42. Inside a Membrane Tank of the Technigaz Type. (GTT.)

As can be seen from the listing above, there was no shortage of inventiveness and determination in the LNG industry. And let us not forget the proposal to build 200,000 m³ LNG submarine tankers, with liquid oxygen tanks to supply the boilers, for the transportation of LNG from North Canada, under the ice pack! Such is the enthusiasm which the prospect of the rapid development of the LNG industry has always generated.

However, all LNG ships ordered within the last 20 years have been of only four different designs:

- The self-supporting spherical tank type B from Kvaerner-Moss.

- The Gaz Transport Membrane system.

- The Technigaz Membrane system.

- The self-supporting prismatic tank type B from Ishikawajima-Harima Industries.

These four designs will be examined in more detail.

43. LNG Tanker of the SPB Tank Type. (IHI.)

5.5.1 SPHERICAL TANKS

The first LNG carrier with spherical tanks was built in the Moss Rosenberg shipyard in Stavenger, Norway, in 1973. This was the 87,600 m³ Norman Lady, with tanks in 9% nickel steel. The Kvaerner-Moss spherical tank design is the only LNG containment system to have been built commercially without prior prototype testing. However, the designer was confident that the extensive studies and supporting test work completed prior to the construction of the first ships had proved that the design was safe and practical. These studies included the following work:

- Study of wave loads and ship motion including shear forces, bending and twisting moments, acceleration and liquid motion in the tanks.

- Study of the connection between tank and support at the equatorial ring by finite element and photo-elastic analysis and fatigue testing.

- Thermal stresses in the tank shell, particularly in the equatorial zone, torsional response of the hull and its effect on the spheres and their supports and stability of the tank and supporting skirt under different loading had been the object of a detailed structural analysis.

- Detailed analysis of the cargo containment system, its insulation and the general arrangement and operation of the cargo equipment.

- Detailed investigation of the properties of 9% nickel steel particularly its fatigue behaviour and crack propagation characteristics under various stress levels.

The Kvaerner-Moss confidence was justified as, at the end of 1999, there were 63 LNG tankers (54% of the total fleet number) of various sizes equipped with spherical tanks in service around the world, with another 8 on order. Sizes vary from 19,000 to 138,000 m³.

Although the two first ships were built with tanks in 9% nickel steel, the design was soon changed to aluminium and all subsequent ships were built with aluminium tanks. Due to the perfect geometrical shape of the sphere, it was easy to carry out finite element calculations to determine the level of stress and the extent of possible crack propagation. Based on these calculations proving that it is impossible for a crack, in any circumstances, to propagate into a catastrophic failure, it was admitted by classification societies and confirmed by the IMO IGC Code that the spherical tank type B does not require a full secondary barrier. The only requirement is for a drip-tray at the bottom of the hold to prevent any possible dripping of cargo, resulting from a limited crack, to damage the ship's structure.

The other main characteristic of the spherical tank designed by Kvaerner-Moss is the way the tank is supported. This is achieved by having a continuous cylindrical, stiffened skirt attached to the equator by a special extrusion allowing the sphere to expand and contract freely with minimum load being applied to the shell. The skirt is itself welded integrally to the structure and is subjected to the hull's deflexions which it has been designed to absorb. The extrusion at the equator of the tank and the top of the skirt are aluminium and the bottom of the skirt is low temperature carbon steel. The link between the two parts is composed of a structural transition joint made of aluminium alloy, titanium, nickel and stainless steel joined together by explosion bonding and a thermal break made of stainless steel to reduce the thermal leak between the tank and the ship structure through the skirt. With this system, it is claimed that boil-off rates as low as 0.10% per day can be achieved.

Tank insulation varies slightly from yard to yard, but it is basically formed of several layers of cellular foam of various compositions, covered by a vapour barrier in aluminium foil or fibreglass to prevent any ingress of moisture inside the insulation when the temperature is lowered. The thickness of the insulation is dependant on the amount of boil-off deemed acceptable for the project for which the ship is built. The holds around the tanks are kept under an atmosphere of either inert gas or dry air.

The Kvaerner Moss spherical tank design continues to enjoy considerable popularity among owners of LNG tonnage and this is confirmed by the steady number of LNG tankers with spherical tanks ordered during the 1990's.

5.5.2 MEMBRANE TANKS

There are two different designs of LNG membrane tanks: the Gaz Transport design and the Technigaz design. Both systems were developed during the 1960's. The first prototype of a Gaz Transport membrane containment system was installed on the 30,000 m³ LPG tanker "Hypolite Worms" in 1967. The first LNG tanker equipped with the full design was the 71,500 m³ "Polar Alaska", delivered by the Kockum shipyard in 1969. The first prototype of a Technigaz membrane was installed on the 630 m³ "Pythagore", delivered in 1965 and used mainly as an LPG and ethylene tanker. The first LNG ship equipped with the full design was the 50,000 m³ "Descartes", delivered in 1971.

44. Spherical Tank. (Kawasaki Heavy Ind.)

Both Gaz Transport and Technigaz designs use thin flexible steel "membranes" to contain the cargo. The membranes are surrounded by insulation material applied directly on the ship's double hull and the weight of the cargo is transmitted through the insulation and supported by the ship's structure. This is as far as the two designs can be compared. The detailed concept and realisation of each system are very different, one of the major differences being the material used to make the actual membrane.

The Gaz Transport system uses a 36% iron-nickel alloy known as Invar, produced by Metal-Imphy. This material has an extremely low expansion coefficient which allows the use of flat panels for the construction of the membrane. This facilitates the welding operations and makes possible the installation of a second membrane, symetrical to the first one, which acts as the secondary barrier. The system includes two layers of insulation,

the first located between the two membranes, the second between the second membrane and the ship's hull. The insulation comprises a series of plywood boxes containing perlite powder. In order that the sealing membranes follow the hull flexing, due to wave motion and cargo pressure, the insulation/membrane interface allows independent movement of one in relation to the other. All the components of the system are integrated in a modular assembly with the size of the insulating boxes (1 × 0.5 × 0.3 metre) corresponding to the width of the membrane streak (0.5 metre × 0.7 millimetre) extending the whole length of the tank. As in the case of spherical tanks, the thickness of the insulation is decided by the level of boil-off required.

The Technigaz system uses a very low carbon content stainless steel. To compensate for movement due to temperature change, orthogonal corrugations, allowing extensive expansion in

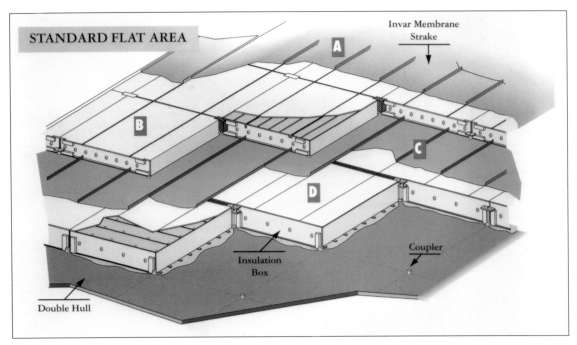

45. Drawing of the Gaz Transport Membrane Tank System. (GTT.)

two directions under a light load, are formed by folding the membrane. The insulation, which, on the first ships, was balsa wood, is now expanded polyurethane foam reinforced with fibreglass and the secondary barrier is made of a composite material, comprising a thin sheet of aluminium glued between two layers of glass cloth. The thickness of the membrane is 1.2 millimetre and that of the insulation is dependant on the expected boil-off.

In both membrane systems, the insulation spaces surrounding the membranes are maintained under an atmosphere of nitrogen and are constantly monitored for any possible presence of methane, which would indicate a leak, however minimal, through the membrane.

The name "membrane", which has been generally adopted to describe this technique, is not necessarily appropriate, as it gives the impression of a sheet of very thin material. Most car makers use body panels 0.7 millimetre thick, the same thickness as the Gaz Transport membrane and almost half that of the Technigaz membrane. [23]

A total of 48 LNG tankers equipped with membrane type tanks were in service in the world at the end of 1999, with another 8 on order. Sizes vary from 18,500 to 138,000 m^3.

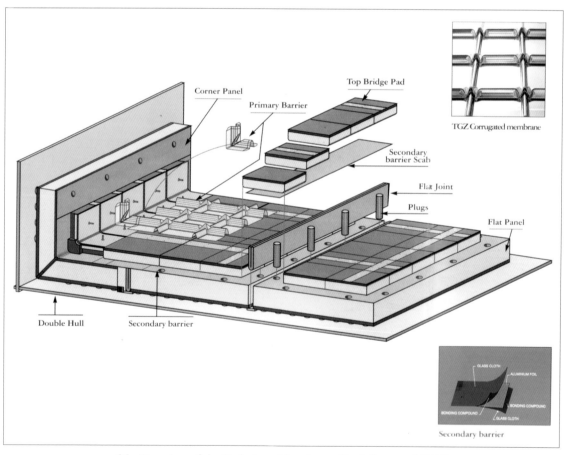

46. Drawing of the Technigaz Membrane Tank System. (GTT.)

After many years of negotiation, Gaz Transport and Technigaz merged in 1994. The new organisation is working hard on developing a new design which will incorporate the best of the two techniques. It is understood that this new design will be ready for commercial use in the first years of the new century. In the meantime, the two existing designs have been regularly improved and are enjoying continued success, as confirmed by the many orders for Gaz Transport and Technigaz LNG tankers placed during the 1990's.

5.5.3 SELF-SUPPORTING PRISMATIC TYPE B (SPB) TANKS

Self-supporting, Prismatic type B tanks were developed by Ishikawajima Harima Heavy Industries (IHI) during the 1980's. This

development was based on the long experience acquired by IHI of building prismatic type A tanks for LPG tankers. The new tanks are very similar to those used in the Conch system, but the development of improved computerised finite element analysis allowed major differences to be introduced:

- The tanks are designed and built to meet IMO's leak-before-failure criteria and to be classified as type B tanks.

- The insulation is attached to the tanks and not to the inner hull, and type B tanks do not require a full secondary barrier but only small leak protection.

The tanks are built of aluminium and very extensive use is made of automatic welding systems. They rest on a number of bottom supports, suitably

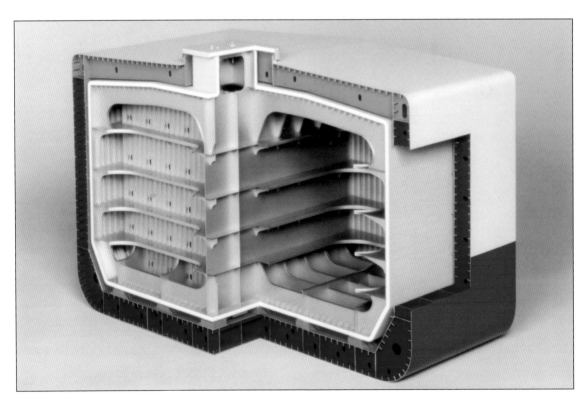

47. Drawing of the SPB Tank system. (IHI.)

insulated from the ship's hull and anti-floating and anti-rolling chocks ensure that they remain in position in all conditions. The insulation is composed of panels of polyurethane foam covered with a vapour protection barrier. A longitudinal bulkhead, equipped with a foot valve, divides the tank in two and transversal swash bulkheads provide the necessary reinforcement. The holds around the tanks are kept under an atmosphere of either inert gas or dry air. The boil-off rate has been set at 0.15% per day.

After numerous presentations of their new LNG containment system to various international conferences, orders for two ships of 87,500 m³ capacity were eventually signed in 1989 for delivery in 1993. Although it is generally agreed that this containment system and the two ships equipped with it are a success, only one other order has been received by IHI for a vessel with SPB tanks. This vessel is an LPG FPSO, now in operation on the West Africa coast.

48. Spherical Tank Transported on a Barge. (The Author.)

Chapter 6
OTHER CHARACTERISTICS SPECIFIC TO LIQUEFIED GAS TANKERS

6.1   GENERAL

Liquefied Petroleum Gas (LPG) Tankers are very similar, in terms of general equipment, to the sophisticated chemical tankers or parcel tankers. They are, as a matter of course, built with high quality materials and fitted with a high level of navigation and communication equipment. Because of the high value of the cargo containment system and other cargo equipment, the ships are expected to last for many years and particular attention is paid to the quality of hull construction and the general corrosion protection. As maintenance of the hull integrity is the key to ship longevity, the corrosion protection of these ships is usually the object of constant regular attention during the ship's life.

Liquefied Natural Gas (LNG) Tankers are slightly different, particularly where their machinery is concerned. As the LNG boil-off is lighter than air at ambient temperature, it has been found convenient to use it as fuel in the ship's machinery and burning it in boilers has, up to now, been found the most practical way of using this available fuel. Onshore installations, natural gas is currently used in diesel engines and gas turbines but this type of machinery has not yet found favour with ship operators.

This is why, to date, all LNG ships but two are equipped with boilers, steam turbo generators for electrical production and steam turbines for propulsion. Furthermore, because the cost of these ships is even higher than that of the LPG ships,

more reliability and a longer life is expected from them and better materials and more precautions are used for their construction.

6.2   RULES AND REGULATIONS

6.2.1   DESIGN AND CONSTRUCTION

Ship design and construction are controlled by a set of comprehensive international rules which are universally accepted. For very specialised ships, such as liquefied gas tankers, the rules are very far-reaching and include detailed coverage of cargo containment systems and other cargo equipment.

These rules are mainly laid down by the International Maritime Organization (IMO). The most important are incorporated in the International Convention for the Safety of Life at Sea (SOLAS), [1] covering the following subjects:

Chapter 1	General Provisions
Chapter 2.1	Design and Construction – Hull, machinery and electrical installations
Chapter 2.2	Design and Construction – Fire protection, detection and extinction
Chapter 3	Life saving appliances and their arrangements
Chapter 4	Radio communications
Chapter 5	Safety at sea and navigation

Chapter 7   Carriage of dangerous goods – Construction and Equipment of Ships Carrying Dangerous Liquid Chemicals in Bulk and Construction and Equipment of Ships Carrying Liquefied Gases in Bulk (IGC Code)

Chapter 9   International Management Code for the Safe Operation of Ships and for Pollution Prevention (ISM Code)

Rule application is controlled and supervised by the Flag State of the ship. A ship's conformity with the rules is confirmed by the delivery of the following certificates:

- Load Line Certificate

- Safety Construction Certificate

- Safety Equipment Certificate

- Safety Radio Equipment Certificate

- Certificate of Fitness for the Carriage of Liquefied Gases in Bulk (or dangerous chemicals in bulk)

- Safety Management Certificate

- MARPOL Certificate

Some Flag States carry out their own inspections and administer their own certification process. However, most Flag States delegate some or all of these tasks to Classification Societies which are then empowered to deliver the certificates in the name of the Flag State.

Classification Societies have included all the SOLAS regulations into their own classification rules. They clarify and complement these rules with their own additions and interpretations. These are mainly detailed considerations on construction materials, strength and buoyancy

49. LNG Tanker Under Construction. (The Author.)

calculations, types of equipment for each type of ship.

To confirm the application of these detailed rules, Classification Societies deliver their own Classification Certificates for hull, machinery and cargo equipment.

All the certificates, whether issued by Flag States or Classification Societies, must be kept valid throughout the active life of the ship by means of periodic inspections. The interval between inspections varies from one year, for the simple ones, up to five years for the more comprehensive checks. The five-year surveys, the so-called Special Surveys, include complete internal re-inspection of most parts of the ships, with detailed checking of the hull thickness, internal condition of the tanks and demonstration of the good operation of all machinery, including electrical, cargo, navigation and communication equipment.

6.2.2 OPERATION AND CREWING

As in the case of ship design and construction, ship operation and crewing are guided by comprehensive sets of International and National Rules.

The new International Management Code for the Safe Operation of Ships and for Pollution Prevention, the ISM Code, now included in Chapter 9 of SOLAS, came into force in July 1998 for certain vessels, including liquefied gas tankers. It gives guidance for establishing methods for the organisation, administration and operation of the ship operating company. These rules are applicable to shore operating offices as well as to ships at sea. After establishing procedures and issuing operating manuals as required by the ISM Code, operating companies and ships must be audited at regular intervals by a representative of the Flag State for confirmation that the rules are known and applied by all members of the company. The ISM Code includes crewing procedures, hiring practices, conditions on board, levels of responsibility, health and safety, etc. which should be clearly specified in the company instructions and regularly enforced. Among other items covered by the ISM Code are cargo handling, maintenance, communication between ship and shore, protection of the environment, master's responsibility. The ISM Code requires that specific procedures and contingency plans be established for different types of emergency situation, including those involving cargo. All personnel on board and in the company offices ashore must be aware of these procedures and trained in applying the contingency plans. The Code requires that operating companies nominate a representative to be personally responsible for the application of the ISM Code.

The International Convention on Standards of Training, Certification and Watch-keeping for Seafarers 1978, [4] as amended by the 1995 STCW Convention, specifies the minimum level of education, experience and training required from officers and ratings on board. Ideally, a liquefied gas ship operator will insist on a standard higher than this minimum. The ship's total complement is specified by National Administrations and is based on the ship operation, both day-to-day and in an emergency situation, bearing in mind the internationally recognised hours of work. The STCW Convention also discusses proficiency in a common language, maximum hours of work and minimum resting time, general health policy, etc. All the requirements of STCW must be incorporated in the ISM procedures mentioned previously.

50. *Cadets in Training. (Petronas Tankers.)*

51. *Cadets in Training. (Petronas Tankers.)*

Chapter 5 of SOLAS controls safety at sea and navigation. Chapter 7 deals with cargo and safety operations on gas and chemical tankers through the BCH and IGC Codes.

The International Convention for Prevention of Pollution from Ships (MARPOL) [2] has been developed following the serious pollution incidents created by large oil tankers in the 1960's and 1970's, and it is administered by the International Maritime Organization (IMO). Annex 1 covers oil pollution from ships. This can have implications for ship bunkering operations. Annex 2, which is in preparation, will cover pollution from cargo which, most of the time, will not directly affect gas tankers. Future additions to MARPOL will relate to quality of discharged ballast waters and air pollution caused by ships.

6.3   CARGO EQUIPMENT

6.3.1   PIPES AND VALVES

Pipes and valves play a very important role on a liquefied gas tanker. The cargo piping is necessary to load and discharge the cargo in port and to maintain the cargo in good condition whilst at sea. The water-ballast piping is necessary to load and discharge ballast water to ensure the stability of the ship. The fire-fighting and spray-water piping are necessary to ensure the safety of the ship in case of fire. The general piping is necessary for all other general operations on board.

The cargo piping and valves are made of materials suitable for the minimum temperatures, maximum pressures and chemical characteristics of the products to be handled. The piping system must be suitably supported and equipped with expansion loops or bellows to compensate for movement due to changes in temperature. The manifolds are used to receive the shore connections for loading and discharging the cargo. There is usually a sufficient number of liquid and vapour manifolds to completely separate the different products that the ship can carry. A remotely actuated isolating valve, the Emergency Shut-Down (ESD) valve, is fitted at the end of each manifold. A similar valve is also fitted at the end of the shore side piping. In case of incident, the ship or the shore can close the two valves remotely to stop the flow of cargo and prevent any leakage. One or several liquid and vapour headers link the manifolds to the tanks with an isolating valve at the connection with each tank. Separate piping networks link the tanks to the reliquefaction equipment, often combined with the spraying/cooling equipment, also to the inerting and aerating system. Each cargo tank and cargo hold or insulation space is fitted with pressure relief valves directly connected to venting masts. Finally, there is the necessary small piping for the control and instrumentation systems.

52. *Relief Valve for Insulation Spaces of a LNG Tanker. (The Author.)*

53. *Cryogenic Valve Being Tested. (KSB-AMRI.)*

The network of water-ballast piping and valves are made of materials showing a good resistance to sea-water corrosion. It allows all ballast tanks on the ship to be filled or emptied at the same time or one by one through pumps located in the engine room or by gravity directly from the sea. The time necessary to fill or empty the ballast tanks is usually based on the time necessary to load or discharge the cargo.

The fire-fighting and water-spray piping and valve networks, also made of materials resistant to sea-water corrosion, must be fire resistant as well. Fire pumps in the engine room provide a good flow of water to the fire-fighting piping, with sufficient pressure to reach all parts of the ship, including the highest point. The spray-water piping network is also supplied by a pump in the engine room. It covers the cargo tank domes, the cargo manifolds, the cargo machinery and control room, the front of the accommodation and the life boats boarding area with a specified quantity of sea-water to help keep all these areas cool in case of fire. It is also used to protect the ship's structure in case of a drop in temperature resulting from cargo leakage and to assist in the vaporisation of leaked cargo.

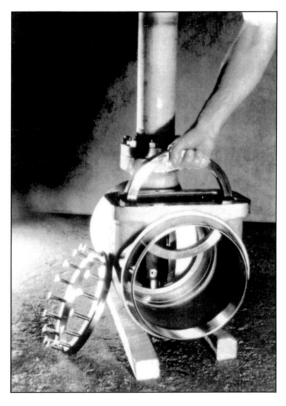

54. Cryogenic Valve Being Serviced.
(KSB-AMRI.)

6.3.2 RELIQUEFACTION PLANTS

Fully-pressurised gas carriers can accommodate the maximum pressure that the cargo will reach during the voyage. LNG carriers use the cargo boil-off as fuel, thus maintaining the tank pressure and temperatures at the required level. All other semi-pressurised and fully-refrigerated LPG carriers must be equipped with reliquefaction plants to control the cargo pressure during the voyage. There are two main types of reliquefaction plant, both designed to perform the following functions:

- Cool down the cargo tanks and associated pipelines before loading.

- Reliquefy the cargo vapour generated by flash evaporation, liquid displacement and boil-off during loading.

- Maintain cargo temperature and pressure within the required levels by reliquefying the boil-off vapour.

a) **Indirect Cycle** – In this system, the cargo vapours are refrigerated and condensed by an external refrigeration system, without being compressed. There are not many ships equipped with such a system, as it requires much greater refrigeration capacity than the direct cycle systems (Fig 6.1).

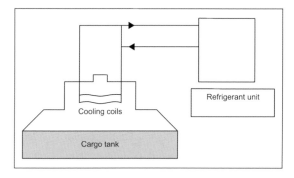

Figure 6.1 Indirect Cooling Cycle. (SIGTTO.)

However the IMO Gas Code requires this type of refrigeration for the carriage of:

- Chlorine

- Ethylene oxide

- Propylene oxide

b) **Direct Cycle** – In this system, the cargo vapours are compressed, condensed and returned to the tank. It is the system found on most ships but it cannot be used with certain gases. Three different types of direct cycle reliquefaction plants are used:

- Single-stage direct cycle - Mainly found on semi-pressurised ships (Fig: 6.2)

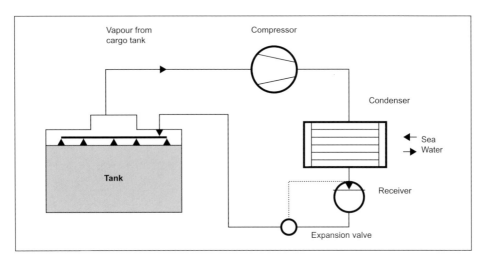

Figure 6.2 Single-Stage Direct Reliquefaction Cycle. (SIGTTO.)

- Two-stage direct cycle – Not very common – The two-stage compression limits the compressor discharge temperature – Used for products such as butadiene and vinyl chloride (Fig: 6.3).

- Cascade direct cycle – Mainly used on fully-refrigerated ships (Fig 6.4)

Up to now the refrigerant R22 was used for the first stage of the cascade. However, according to the Montreal protocol, this product will be phased out by the year 2020 at the latest. A recent trend is to use a closed circuit of propane instead of R 22.

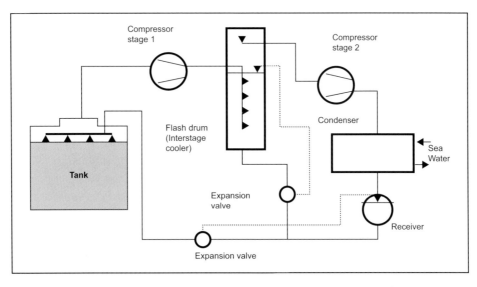

Figure 6.3 Two Stage Direct Reliquefaction Cycle with Inter-Stage Cooler. (SIGTTO.)

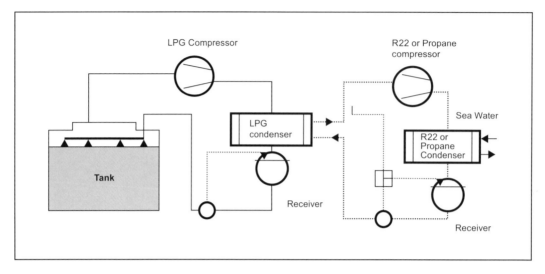

Figure 6.4 Simple Cascade Reliquefaction System. (SIGTTO.)

55. Booster Pump. (The Author.)

6.3.3 PUMPS AND COMPRESSORS

Some fully pressurised ships are only equipped with compressors to discharge their cargo. They take vapour from one tank, compress it and push it to the top of the tank to be discharged. Most modern ships, however, have, in addition, one or more booster pumps to speed up discharging operations.

Semi-pressurised ships are all equipped with at least one deepwell pump per tank. This type of pump has the electric or hydraulic motor on top of the tank dome and a long shaft to drive the pump located at the bottom of the tank. The two critical points of these pumps are the tightness of the shaft inlet into the tank and the guiding of the shaft over its full length to avoid any vibration. In case of failure of one of the pumps, the compressors can be used, as described above for pressurised ships. On these semi-pressurised ships, except for the very occasional emergency discharge, compressors are used only for reliquefaction and during inerting/aerating operations. Most of the semi-pressurised ships are equipped with booster pumps and cargo heaters, using sea water as a heating medium, to allow the discharge of cargo at ambient temperature into pressurised storage.

The fully-refrigerated ships are equipped with either deepwell pumps or submerged pumps. Submerged pumps have the electric motor built into the pump in one unit which is located at the bottom of the tank. This is no problem for LPG, LNG and most of the petrochemical gases which are dielectric. For ships transporting ammonia, however, special types of submerged pumps are required. Due to the low tank pressure on fully-refrigerated ships, compressors cannot be used as an emergency discharging method. It is necessary to have two pumps per tank. On tanks with a longitudinal bulkhead, a foot valve allows the two halves to communicate and then one pump can discharge the whole tank. Another method is to have an emergency pump installed in a column equipped with a foot valve. The column can be emptied and inerted with nitrogen under pressure and, with the valve closed, the emergency pump can be installed. Submerged pumps are difficult to access for maintenance and, although they are normally very reliable, damage occurs very quickly if they are run dry, even very briefly. For very large LPG ships, a choice must be made between deepwell pumps with very long shafts or submerged pumps. Fully-refrigerated ships are also equipped with a cargo booster pump/heater combination to be able to discharge their cargo into pressurised storage, if required.

LNG ships are all equipped with two submerged pumps per tank. Membrane tanks are usually equipped with a tube to install an emergency pump in case of failure of the two pumps in one tank. If this happens on board a ship equipped with self-supporting tanks, it is possible, using the compressors, to raise the pressure in one tank sufficiently to discharge that cargo. This, however, is only permitted if the tanker is in calm waters.

Some of the petrochemical gases carried by LPG tankers can react with the lubricating oil used in the cargo compressors. Most ships use oil free compressors, where cylinders are not lubricated and the compressed gas is completely separate from the crankcase containing the lubricating oil. Ships equipped with a two-stage reliquefaction system usually have a first-stage centrifugal compressor and a second-stage oil-free reciprocating compressor. Large ships are equipped with high-flow, centrifugal blowers to deal with cargo vapour and also to speed up the

56. *Deep Well Pump*

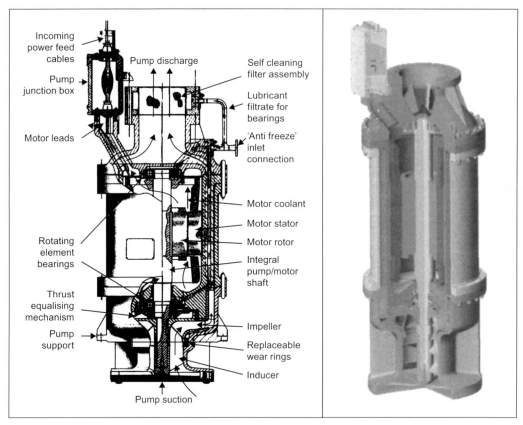

Incoming power feed cables

Pump junction box

Motor leads

Rotating element bearings

Thrust equalising mechanism

Pump support

Pump discharge

Self cleaning filter assembly

Lubricant filtrate for bearings

'Anti freeze' inlet connection

Motor coolant

Motor stator

Motor rotor

Integral pump/motor shaft

Impeller

Replaceable wear rings

Inducer

Pump suction

57. and 58. LNG Submerged Pumps. (EBARA Cryodynamics.)

59. Cargo Oil-Free Compressor. (The Author.)

gas freeing/inerting operation. LNG ships are also fitted with high-flow centrifugal blowers to return cargo vapour ashore during loading, to deal with the boil-off at sea and to warm up the tanks prior to inerting.

6.3.4 CARGO QUANTITY MEASUREMENT - CUSTODY TRANSFER

Cargo quantity measurement is a major concern on all liquefied gas ships as the quantity of cargo loaded or discharged is usually measured on board. During a ship's construction, the volume of the cargo tanks is accurately measured by an expert surveyor, approved by the customs authority of the country where the ship is registered or where the cargo is regularly loaded or discharged. The tank calibration tables, usually showing the level at every centimetre, include corrections for temperature and for any list and trim. Each tank is equipped with level, pressure and temperature gauges which have a declared accuracy at the normal temperature of operation and which are regularly recalibrated under the supervision of an approved expert. Level gauges can be float, capacitance or radar type. The slip tubes used on early ships are no longer authorised as they could not operate without some cargo being released to the outside. Level readings are usually taken remotely and, on recent ships, they are processed through a computer. All necessary corrections are integrated and the final cargo volume or weight is calculated automatically.

The complete system is known as the custody transfer system and includes all equipment used to obtain the necessary measurements and calculate the results.

Calculations of cargo quantities done on board, most of the time under the supervision of an approved surveyor, are used to establish the commercial documents required by the ship owners and the cargo receivers.

6.3.5 INERT GAS AND NITROGEN

The very high level of safety achieved by liquefied gas tankers is partly due to the fact that, when on board, the cargo is never in contact with air and, therefore, the chances of a fire or explosion are very remote. This is easily achieved during normal operation, when ships carry the same type of cargo over long periods. When, however, it is necessary to clean the tanks prior to the loading of a different type of cargo or to carry out repairs, the tanks must be opened and consequently air is introduced into the system. In such cases, inert gas is used to replace the hydrocarbon gas and remove the fire or explosion risks before the introduction of air.

Inert gas is the exhaust gas resulting from the combustion of oil in a special inert gas generator. Low sulphur gas oil is used and special precautions are taken to ensure a controlled content of oxygen and pollutants, such as carbon monoxide (CO) or nitrogen and sulphur oxides (Nox, Sox). The size of the generator depends on the volume of inert gas required and this, in turn, depends on the size of the ship. Generators up to 15,000 m^3/h are in operation. The inert gas produced is a mixture of mainly nitrogen with approximately 15% of carbon dioxide, between 0.5 and 3% of oxygen, a small amount of water vapour and traces of CO, Nox and Sox. The oxygen content can be adjusted as required, within certain limits, and the gas is passed through coolers and dryers to remove as much water vapour as possible before it is sent to the tanks. Theory shows that a mixture of hydrocarbon and oxygen containing less than 10% to 12% oxygen is not flammable. However, for safety reasons, inert gas with an oxygen content of around 3% is generally used. When there is only a few percent of hydrocarbon left in the tanks, air can be introduced prior to opening the tank. Before loading a new cargo, the reverse operation is

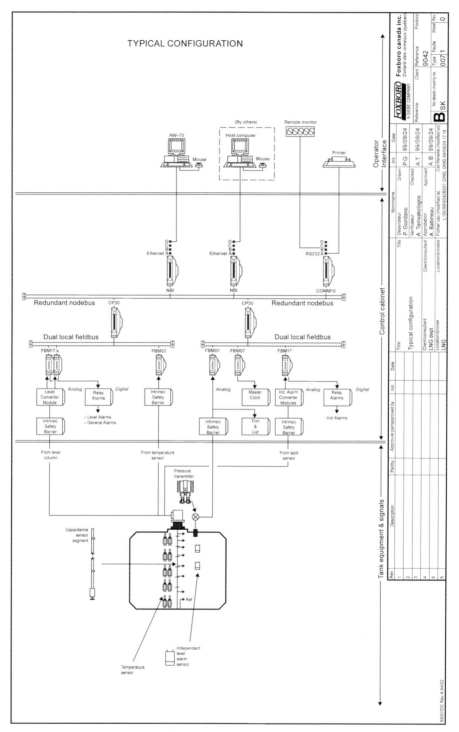

60. Drawing of a Custody Transfer System. (Foxboro.)

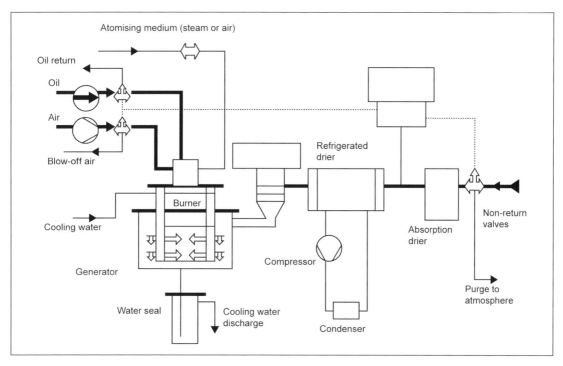

Figure 6.5 Inert-Gas Generator – Flow Diagram. (SIGTTO.)

carried out. Air is displaced by inert gas until only a low percentage of oxygen remains prior to introducing hydrocarbon products into the tank.

Some of the petrochemical gases react with oxygen and, in such cases, very low levels of oxygen are called for. When it is necessary to have oxygen levels below 0.5%, pure nitrogen is used. This is usually delivered from shore in the form of liquid nitrogen which is vaporised before being taken on board. However, nitrogen can also be produced on board using nitrogen membrane generators. In these generators, compressed air is pushed through a special membrane which allows the nitrogen molecules to go through but retains the molecules of oxygen. These systems have seen a very rapid development in recent years and units capable of producing several thousand cubic metres per hour are now in service.

61. Nitrogen Generator. (The Author.)

Ammonia reacts with carbon dioxide and inert gas cannot be used to displace ammonia. In early years, ammonia was directly removed by dry air. However, current practice is to use CO_2-free inert gas either from shore or from a nitrogen membrane generator. This has the added advantage of avoiding the introduction of moisture into the tanks, which is always a possibility when using air.

On LNG ships, inert gas is used to displace methane before opening the tanks and also to maintain an inert atmosphere in the holds or insulation spaces around the tanks. However the carbon dioxide contained in inert gas freezes at –56°C which is much higher than the LNG temperature of –162°C. To avoid this problem, the tanks are warmed to ambient temperature prior to the introduction of inert gas for the displacement of methane and nitrogen is used to maintain the inert atmosphere around the tanks. Up to 10 years ago, all LNG ships were fitted with a small tank of liquid nitrogen for this purpose and it was necessary to supply the ships

with liquid nitrogen at frequent intervals. With the development of the nitrogen membrane generators, this is no longer necessary.

6.4 SAFETY EQUIPMENT

6.4.1 EMERGENCY SHUT-DOWN SYSTEMS (ESDS)

This is an important part of the safety equipment specific to liquefied gas tankers. The ESDS, if activated, will stop cargo pumps and compressors, shut down the gas burning on LNG ships and close designated cargo valves, including the manifold loading and discharge valves. The system can be activated by hand from various places in the cargo area or automatically through set points from the control system or, in case of fire, by melting plugs located in the cargo area.

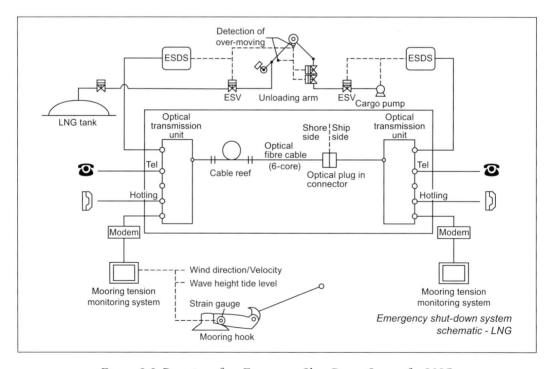

Figure 6.6 Drawing of an Emergency Shut Down System for LNG.

The loading and discharging terminals are also equipped with an ESD System designed to protect the shore loading/discharging arms and hoses and other equipment in case of a pressure surge from the ship or against possible drifting of the ship when connected alongside. The shore ESD system has usually two levels of safety: ESDI, activated when the ship's movement is limited to a pre-set level and which stops pumps and compressors and closes the manifold valves on board and ashore, and ESD2, activated when the ship's movement continues and risks damaging the arms. ESD2 will automatically close the loading/discharging arms' dry-break coupling valves and disconnect the dry-break couplings, protecting the arms from permanent damage.

62. Dry-Break Coupling. (FMC.)

When a liquefied gas tanker is connected to a terminal, it is strongly recommended to link the ship and the terminal ESD's. If this is done, the ship can stop the terminal's pumps in case of an incident during loading, the terminal can stop the ship's pumps in case of an incident during discharging and the loading/discharging arms can be isolated and disconnected very quickly in case of unexpected displacement of the ship alongside the terminal, before a serious leak of cargo occurs. In the early years, the link between ship and shore ESD was made through an air pressure hose. In case of movement between ship and jetty, the hose would, in theory, be damaged and the loss of air pressure would activate the ESD. This was very basic and has now been replaced by transmission through electric signal, fibre-optic signal or radio signal. Small LPG terminals do not all have a linked ESD system but, in some terminals, the shore gives a pendant to the ship during loading and the ship gives a pendant to the shore during discharging. These pendants are an extension of each party's ESD systems.

Large LNG terminals equipped with fibre-optic transmission can also use it for the connection of several voice and electronic transmission channels between ship and shore.

To assist connection and disconnection of the ship and shore cargo-piping, some terminals have hard arms equipped with Powered Emergency Release Coupling (PERC). This equipment replaces nuts and bolts to establish tight connections of the shore arm flanges to the ship's manifold flange. It can be activated manually or hydraulically.

Hooks receiving the ship's mooring lines on LNG jetties are equipped with automatic release couplings set to release at a certain level of line tension, to avoid the mooring lines breaking, should the ship's mooring become unbalanced or overloaded due to strong winds and currents.

63. Powered Emergency Release Coupling (PERC). (SIGTTO.)

6.4.2 OTHER SAFETY EQUIPMENT

The IGC Code specifies in great detail the minimum inventory of safety equipment that must be carried by liquefied gas carriers. It is a comprehensive list and includes equipment for fire protection, fire-fighting, gas detection and individual personnel protection.

Engine rooms, cargo machinery rooms and accommodation must have fire detection equipment and fire alarms. The entrance to cargo electrical machinery areas must be equipped with special over-pressure ventilation systems, including fail-safe arrangements. There are provisions for stopping the whole ventilation of the ship from one central point. The water fire-fighting and water-spray systems must be remotely controlled and a fixed dry chemical powder system must be installed on deck for extinguishing gas fires. Gas analysers must be located at strategic points in the cargo area and other areas on board and must automatically warn of any presence of gas. Individual protection equipment must include a specified number of self-contained compressed-air breathing apparatus, special chemical protection suits adapted to the cargoes carried, decontamination showers and eye-wash fountains, complete fire-fighting suits, individual gas and oxygen analysers, oxygen reanimation equipment, stretcher, portable ventilation fans, etc.

There should be evidence that all the safety equipment is in working order and properly maintained. The whole crew must be familiar with the operation of all this equipment and training exercises must be held frequently. [9.16]

Chapter 7
PORTS, TERMINALS AND JETTIES

7.1 REDUCING THE LEVEL OF RISKS

The shipping industry requires ships to transport goods and ports to provide safe and protected locations in which to load or discharge these goods. Ports must be easily accessible to ships, protected from the weather and must enable easy collection and distribution of the goods being loaded and discharged. This statement is good for all types of shipping and therefore applies to the shipping of liquefied hydrocarbon gases.

Berths and jetties, specially equipped to load or discharge liquefied hydrocarbon gases, can be located in different types of port. These can be general cargo ports, where a special area is reserved for petroleum products in general or liquefied gases only, or they can be part of a refinery or chemical plant, or within specialised terminals, such as LNG jetties located near LNG liquefaction plants or vaporisation/distribution plants. Loading jetties are, in general, close to production or manufacturing areas, such as production wells, refineries or chemical plants. Discharging jetties are close to distribution points and commercial markets, such as chemical plants, power plants and densely populated areas.

Whatever their location, these facilities must be suitably sited and equipped to allow safe loading and discharging of all products carried by the liquefied gas tankers calling at them. The most critical period of the shipping phase is when the ship approaches the port and berth at the jetty to load or discharge cargo. The frequency of marine accidents is greater in port than on the open sea. From the time the ship approaches the port area until the time she leaves, the responsibility for the various sequences of operation is spread over several groups of people, with different backgrounds and different training. To ensure a continuous safe and reliable operation, extensive planning and preparation are necessary. The level of marine risk must be quantified and risk-reduction methods must be applied to the design, construction and operation of liquefied gas terminals and jetties.

Assessments of risk conducted by the industry have concluded that the most significant hazards facing liquefied gas ships and terminals involve releases, both small and large of liquid gas. Vaporised LPG and LNG are not toxic so fire and deflagration are the most important potential consequences of a spillage. Other chemical gases and ammonia, however, can be highly toxic, even in very small quantities, and, in such cases, the danger is increased by their toxicity or corrosive nature.

Available measures to reduce these risks can be summarised as follows:

- The location of the storage facility and of the terminal and jetty must be carefully selected and evaluated when determining the level of risk to be considered for each plant.

- Good design and safe construction, based on reliable experience and on risk calculation methods, are essential factors in the limitation of the risks. High quality materials must be used throughout as a matter of principle and the influence of human judgement should be carefully assessed.

64. LNG Tanker Arriving at a LNG Receiving Terminal. (The Author.)

- Operational procedures, including planning, preparation, supervision, maintenance of equipment, training, avoidance of human error and protection against sabotage, must be carefully prepared.

7.2 LOCATION, DESIGN AND CONSTRUCTION

When attempting to determine a suitable location for a liquefied gas loading or discharging terminal, marine experts will be particularly concerned about the following points:

- Sheltered water with the required depth

- Safe access to the sea

- Protection from the strongest weather effects (wind, waves and current)

- Achieving immediate adjacency to the liquefied gas terminal

- Good mooring points available for all intended vessels

- Fender positions and quality

- Finding an earthquake-free area and using earthquake-proof structures

- Avoiding close proximity to other industrial areas.

In view of the difficulty of escaping from basic site location factors, it is probably impossible to find an ideal solution. The challenge, however, is to limit marine and natural risks while maintaining the location of storage tanks, terminal and jetty within practicable limits.

When choosing the position of a jetty, sheltered locations must be favoured in order to limit dynamic forces caused by sea-waves. Areas where passing ships present collision or ranging risks must also be avoided.

There are no international rules applicable to the design, construction and equipment of liquefied gas terminals. Designers must rely on national regulations, if any are available, or on publications from international professional organisations [8, 17, 18, 19]. The existing standards provide basic guidelines for securing a safe berth but they are rarely sufficient to afford the assurance required for liquefied gas, therefore risk-related methods addressing the incident probability must be adopted as well.

The type and quantity of equipment to be installed should be carefully considered in the context of risk reduction.

The design of a port receiving liquefied gas carriers must include for the complete passage from the port approaches to the jetty, suitably sized access channels and turning areas to provide the ship with safe transit through the port. Additional facilities such as Vessel Traffic Systems (VTS), escort boats and ship speed-of-approach indicators may, also assist. Each port should be inspected for dangers which would cause critical impact in case of grounding or collision, whether with another ship or a foreign object. When considering collision or grounding hazards for most liquefied gas hull designs, methods are available to estimate what damage may result in a large release of liquid gas. This is achieved by identification of the energy necessary

to penetrate the ship's hull. The position of the cargo tanks at a safe distance from the hull makes their possible damage unlikely. However, based on these results, criteria for accident severity in terms of ship speed can be set to levels where rupture of the cargo containment system is virtually impossible. [24, 25]

The design of liquefied gas jetties should ensure that gas carriers can securely and safely lie alongside while transferring cargo. Fenders and mooring points must be adequately sized and positioned to provide the size of vessel expected to use the berth with good rest positions. Mooring studies should be carried out for all vessels expected to berth at the jetty. This will ensure the loading connections remain secure and will minimise the risk of arm or hose rupture caused by ship movement. The addition of an Emergency Shut-Down System (ESDS) and a Powered Emergency Release Coupling (PERC) fitted within the arm will allow safe, quick and automatic disconnection should a liquefied gas carrier move outside predetermined limits in relation to the jetty. This provides an extra level of safety to prevent possible cargo spillage.

The design of the terminal must ensure that the fire protection equipment installed is appropriate to the type and volume of cargo to be transferred and to the environment surrounding the terminal.

The risk of cargo vapour ignition must be evaluated on a port by port basis. In the event of release of liquefied gas, the spread of a gas cloud can cover a considerable distance. When estimating the possible spread of gas clouds, the type of gas, the spill rate and duration, the climatic conditions and the local topography must all be taken into consideration. Ignition controls must be far-reaching and suitable emergency procedures must be in place to prevent contamination of personnel or the public, in case of leakage of toxic gas.

65. LNG Loading Terminal. (Malaysia LNG.)

Terminal design should also include the setting of operating criteria, expressed in terms of wind speed, wave height and current for the maximum forces allowed for the range of liquefied gas carriers planned for that terminal. This should take into account the different characteristics of the vessels and their mooring equipment. Equipment to monitor effectively and accurately the environmental conditions should be available to allow these operating criteria to be properly observed. The same criteria should also be used to determine the number and power of tugs needed for berthing and unberthing manoeuvring.

Human error is unfortunately contributing to the large majority of industrial casualties. In seeking operational solutions for liquefied gas ports, terminals and jetties, the design methods adopted should not, as far as is possible, rely on the sole contribution of human judgement.

7.3 OPERATIONAL PROCEDURES

In the same way as there are no international rules governing the design and construction of terminals, the operation of ports, terminals and the training of their personnel are at the discretion of the operators, relying on national regulations, when available, or on publications from international professional organisations [8, 11]. Operating and emergency procedures remain the decision of the operators. Quality certification, such as ISO 9000, provides useful help in this respect. The operational procedures in place at liquefied gas terminals must include accident prevention and control measures focusing on reducing the probability of a collision, grounding or accidental leakage alongside the berth, minimising the effects of any occurrence of these incidents.

IMO has published recommendations for the transit of dangerous goods in port areas, which are a guide for safe operations [5]. These recommendations are directed at the following organisations:

- National and Regional Maritime Bodies
- Port Authorities
- Local Fire and Salvage Teams
- Terminal Management
- Liquefied Gas Carrier Managers and Crews

These organisations must be aware of the following:

- The characteristics of liquefied gas carriers
- The nature of possible accidents
- The likely consequences
- The actions that can practically and usefully be taken.

When a liquefied gas carrier calls at a terminal to load or discharge, the terminal must ensure, as part of their responsibility towards the ship, that its personnel possess an adequate understanding of ship procedures and cargo handling processes. Similarly, a liquefied gas carrier crew requires a good appreciation of the systems employed at the terminal, both for cargo handling and safety. General experience throughout the industry shows that a common approach helps improve

the safety of operation and reduces the language barriers.

Exchange of information between ship and terminal must start well ahead of the ship's visit. This exchange of information is generally made easier and more efficient if the ship and the terminal have prepared information manuals to provide both parties with all necessary technical and operational information, including guidelines for both routine and emergency situations. This exchange of information continues after ship berthing, at a pre-operation meeting attended by the two persons responsible for the ship and for the terminal operations. The international safety check-list is completed and discussed during the meeting, as well as such important topics as the language to be used, the communication to be maintained between ship and shore throughout the operation, the basic procedures and the emergency procedures used by both parties.

When a liquefied gas carrier arrives at, departs from, or is alongside a terminal for cargo transfer, three organisations are directly responsible for implementing the measures necessary to ensure a safe operation:

- The Port Authority
- The Terminal Management
- The Liquefied Gas Carrier Management

The Port Authority must have all necessary information on the vessels using the port, the cargo they carry, details of the navigation through the port, the weather conditions and the assistance available to the ships. Based on this information and on local conditions, special regulations and provisions may be introduced. These may include the control of the transit of gas carriers through the port, provision for pilotage, tug and escort boats, confirmation that the terminals are providing facilities appropriate to the cargo and that ships visiting the port are in good condition with well-trained crews. Further regulations and provisions will ensure that, while a liquefied gas carrier is alongside for loading or discharging, adequate precautions are taken to prevent accidents. These should include confirmation that the liquefied gas carriers are fit for cargo operation, that their crews are aware of all port and terminal requirements, that communication with the terminal is well established, that all cargo operating procedures, as well as emergency procedures, are in place and understood by all parties involved.

The Terminal Management will wish to consider, in conjunction with the Port Authority, what information is required for an arriving liquefied gas carrier, for example any deficiencies in manoeuvring or mooring capabilities, in addition to the routine operation data. When the liquefied gas carrier is alongside, the Terminal Management is responsible for issuance and enforcement of ship/shore requirements which will maintain safety levels sufficient to ensure the protection of the terminal facilities and to satisfy the requirements of the Port Authority. The Terminal Management should ascertain, in co-operation with the Liquefied Gas Carrier Management, that the ship is ready to proceed with cargo operations, that the procedures for cargo and emergency operations are in place and have been agreed by ship and terminal, that

proper channels of communication between ship and terminal have been established and tested and that all necessary safety precautions have been confirmed as recommended by the International Ship/Shore Safety Check List for Gas Carriers [16].

The Liquefied Gas Carrier Management should be fully aware of all information pertaining to the particular port, such as port entry and traffic control requirements, adequate and corrected charts and publications and any other information specifically requested. Liquefied Gas Carrier Management should also consider measures which will ensure their vessels conduct proper passage planning to and from the berth and bridge team-work procedures, especially with regard to liaison with pilots. Liquefied Gas Carrier Management will equally wish to avoid accidents while its gas carrier is alongside. In addition to having an understanding of those items relating to terminal management, they should consider how best to ensure that the liquefied gas carrier personnel is fully experienced in the procedure to be carried out, that they are aware and ready to comply with all the agreed safety precautions, that they maintain permanently open communications with the terminal and that there will always be sufficient personnel on board to cope with any possible emergency, including moving the vessel out, if necessary.

66. LNG Tanker Berthing at a LNG Receiving Terminal. (The Author.)

Chapter 8
SHORE STORAGE TANKS

8.1 GENERAL

Liquefied hydrocarbon gases require storage facilities ashore, both at the production end and at the distribution end. Storage is required at the production point so that the plant can continue production while waiting for the ship which will transport the gas. It is also required at the distribution point, to allow the ship to discharge its full cargo and return to the loading port without delay, to store the product pending its regular use and to keep a sufficient inventory ready for a period of high demand and higher selling price. Some countries, like Japan, also keep a strategic stock of liquefied gas to guarantee continued availability in case of possible interruption of supply.

In the early years, shore storage tanks held products at ambient temperature in pressurised conditions. For reasons similar to those explained earlier with regards to the ships, pressurised shore tanks were of simple design and small capacity.

The development of transport in fully refrigerated condition and the consequent increase in the size of ships meant that shore tanks had to become much larger and so different construction techniques evolved for cryogenic shore tanks. It started with the single containment tank, followed by the double containment tank and the double integrity or full containment tank and the membrane tank. Large capacity underground storage for LPG was also developed. More recently, the very rapid growth of the LNG trade gave further opportunity for the construction of very large above-ground and in-ground tanks.

The development of shore storage tanks has been further driven by the concerns of regulatory agencies and large consumers for safety and environmental considerations. There have been, through the years, several accidents which, unfortunately, resulted in the total destruction of plants and loss of human lives. These accidents have shown that fire hazards are the greatest risk and that the location and fire protection of liquefied gas tanks should be carefully evaluated.

8.2 STORAGE UNDER PRESSURE AT AMBIENT TEMPERATURE

Storage in these conditions can be provided in the following tanks:

- Spherical or horizontal cylindrical tanks above ground, for LPG and chemical gases

- Mounded horizontal cylindrical tanks, mostly for LPG

- Underground storage caverns for LPG

8.2.1 SPHERICAL AND HORIZONTAL CYLINDRICAL TANKS ABOVE GROUND

These tanks are used at refineries, chemical plants, small or medium size import and export terminals, industrial sites, bottling plants, etc,. They can accommodate LPG and the full range of chemical hydrocarbon gases, as well as ammonia. Pressurised tanks are of small capacity when compared to large refrigerated tanks. The largest pressurised spheres can only have a capacity up to 5,000 m³, but it is possible to create storage plants of reasonable size by grouping a number of spheres or cylindrical tanks.

The design and construction of pressurised tanks must follow recognised pressure vessel codes, such as British Standard BS 5500 or American Standard ASME Boiler and Pressure Vessel Code Section VIII. Each tank must be equipped with at least one pressure relief valve connected directly to the vapour space, a level gauge, pressure and temperature indicators and a high level alarm adjusted to the maximum permissible level.

The lay-out of the storage area must be such that, even if the product should leak from one tank and ignite, it will not put at risk other tanks or equipment in the storage area or people and industrial equipment in adjacent areas.

Following a small number of very spectacular accidents, the storage of liquefied gas is now subject to stricter controls. In Europe, the amended "Seveso Directive", covering major hazard sites, requires the distances previously allowed between each storage tank within the plant and between the plant and other industrial areas and public facilities to be increased. It also gives guidance on the complete lay-out of the plant, the type of fire-fighting equipment required and specifies that each tank must be easily accessible for fire-fighting.

8.2.2 MOUNDED HORIZONTAL CYLINDRICAL TANKS

Most countries specify that pressurised horizontal cylindrical tanks above a certain size are no longer allowed to be installed above ground. Some countries do not allow tanks of this type to be installed above ground at all. They must

67. Horizontal Cylindrical Tank. (SIGTTO.)

be mounded under earth cover protection. The earth cover protects them from being engulfed by flames or from the heat of an adjacent fire so that the BLEVE form of catastrophic failure is impossible. Minimum distances between each tank or group of tanks are specified.

Another advantage of mounded tanks is protection from sun radiation which reduces the rise of the product temperature. One disadvantage, however, is the difficulty to protect tanks against corrosion and to inspect their external parts.

Certain countries specify a maximum size for pressurised spherical tanks in order to reduce the risks in case of fire. Each gas storage vessel and every bulk loading or discharge facility must be provided with a fire-protection system, which will ensure that tanks maintain their structural integrity under fire conditions. This can be by location, insulation or by the use of cooling water. All above-ground pressure tanks must be protected by fixed spray-water systems.

8.2.3 UNDERGROUND CAVERNS

Pressurised LPG may also be stored in underground caverns, either leached from salt deposits or mined from rock formations. The caverns are set at a depth sufficient for the head of the water-table to be greater than the pressure of the stored product. Leakage of products into the rock strata is prevented by the pressure surrounding the cavern. The inflow of ground water is collected and pumped to the surface. The stored product is discharged from the cavern by means of submerged pumps. This is a very safe way of accommodating large quantities of products and a number of very large mined underground caverns have been created in recent years.

8.3 STORAGE IN SEMI-PRESSURISED SPHERES

Spheres for the storage of semi-pressurised LPG, chemical hydrocarbon gases and ammonia can accommodate up to 5,000 tonnes of cargo at temperatures as low as $-50°C$. The spheres must be insulated and the internal pressure must be controlled by means of a reliquefaction plant. They present a much reduced risk in case of fire compared to the pressurised spheres. This is due to their lower operating pressure and the good protection against radiation from any adjacent fire, provided by the insulation. These semi-pressurised spheres can be found in much the same places as pressurised tanks and are a choice containment for chemical gases which have to be kept at low temperature.

68. Spherical Tanks. (SIGTTO.)

8.4 STORAGE AT ATMOSPHERIC PRESSURE IN REFRIGERATED CONDITION

8.4.1 DIFFERENT TYPES OF REFRIGERATED STORAGE TANKS

There are three main groups of refrigerated tanks for LPG, ethylene and LNG:

- Above-ground tanks. This is the original type of refrigerated tank. They may be single containment, double containment or double integrity or full containment. These tanks may be used for LPG, ethylene or LNG.

- In-ground tanks. The in-ground tank consists of a concrete ring section covered with insulation and a stainless steel or Invar membrane. These tanks are expensive to construct and are generally used for LNG.

- In-pit or semi-buried. This is a hybrid of the two previous types, usually double integrity or full containment type and mainly used for LPG and LNG.

a) *Above-Ground Tanks* – Above-ground tanks were originally developed for oil storage. It is by far the most common type of refrigerated tank in use for liquefied gases. The first cylindrical tanks of this type to be built for liquefied gases were commissioned in the late 1950's for the Algeria-UK and Algeria-France LNG projects. Since then, many similar tanks of varying sizes have been built for LPG, ethylene and LNG.

The tank sits on a foundation slab, which may be in contact with the ground or supported on piles, allowing an air gap underneath. If the slab is in contact with the ground, a heating system must be provided to prevent the ground from freezing. This could make the ground heave and so damage the tank foundations.

69. Above Ground Refrigerated Tank. (SIGTTO.)

This type of tank can accommodate single containment, double containment or double integrity or full containment systems. They are simple and reasonably cheap to build and benefit from the considerable experience gained in the construction of traditional oil storage tanks.

The down side is that they are highly visible, which can raise environmental problems; The possibility of liquid spillage in case of catastrophic failure, their vulnerability to radiant heat in case of adjacent fire and possible missile damage are other potential concerns.

b) *In-Ground Tanks* – In-ground tanks are built within a ring section made of reinforced concrete reaching deep underground to the watertight clay or rock level. The bottom of the tank is also reinforced concrete. Load-bearing insulation lines the concrete wall and supports a membrane which can be a "flat" sheet of Invar or a "corrugated" sheet of stainless steel ASTM 304A, in accordance with the Gaz Transport or Technigaz techniques previously described in Chapter 5. Very few tanks have been built

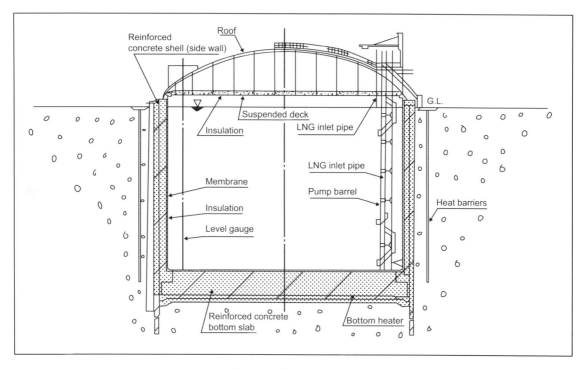

Figure 8.1 A 140,000 m³ In-ground Tank. (SIGTTO.)

using the Gaz Transport technique, but a large number use the Technigaz technique, or similar, adapted by Japanese constructors. The top of the tank can be carbon steel or concrete supporting the insulation There is a gas-tight seal with the side membrane making a gas-free insulation space which can be monitored for leakage in the membrane.

This type of tank is very expensive to build and is generally used for storing LNG. It is extensively used in Japan and Korea as it is well protected against earthquakes. Due to the low level of the tank roof, it is also quite inconspicuous.

Early examples of under-ground tanks built in Europe and Algeria had no membrane or insulation, relying on frozen clay to contain the LNG. This was not successful as it resulted in advancing frozen ground, creating serious ground heave. Those tanks were decommissioned after

less than ten years' operation and much time and cost were spent on heating and cleaning the contaminated areas.

Later tanks had heating systems installed both around the concrete skirt and under the tank bottom. The largest tank of this type has recently been commissioned in Japan, with a capacity of 200,000 m³.

70. In Ground Tank. (SIGTTO.)

The advantage of this type of tank is a very high level of safety. The unstressed membrane prevents possible crack propagation and allows for rapid cool-down/warm-up operations if required. There is no possibility of catastrophic liquid spillage due to containment failure, a good protection against earthquakes, discreet sighting, low exposure to radiant heat in case of adjacent fire and less exposure to impact. There is no limit to the possible tank size.

The disadvantages are duration and high cost of construction and the need to maintain the heating system at all times.

c) ***In-Pit or Semi-Buried Tanks*** – These tanks are a compromise between the above ground type and the in-ground type. They present better safety protection than the above-ground and they are not as expensive to build as the in-ground tanks.

Catastrophic failure with large release of liquid would not be possible with semi-buried type tanks and this type of tank presents good protection against adjacent fire radiation. They would, however, not be as well protected as the in-ground tanks in case of earthquake.

All tanks built as in-pit or semi-buried have been, up to now, of the double integrity type.

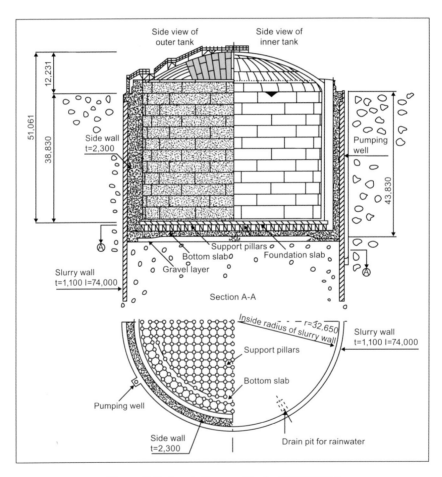

Figure 8.2 In-pit Storage Tank. (SIGTTO.)

71. In Pit Tank. (SIGTTO.)

8.4.2 DIFFERENT TYPES OF CONTAINMENT SYSTEMS

a) *Single Containment* – These tanks were developed from the original, traditional, oil tanks. They were the first refrigerated tanks to be built for LPG as well as for LNG. The tanks consist of:

- A cylindrical metallic wall with a vertical axis built of suitable material designed to withstand the hydrostatic load of the

stored cargo at its minimum temperature and at the maximum storage pressure.

- A flat metallic bottom.

- A self-supporting metallic spherical dome.

- Insulation made of polyurethane foam with vapour barrier located outside the cylindrical wall and inside the dome. The insulation underneath the flat bottom is usually glass foam.

In early tanks, the insulation was left exposed to atmospheric elements and the side wall was generally penetrated by an outlet pipe. Later, an outer envelope, made of thinner carbon steel, was fitted to protect the insulation, frequently consisting of perlite in bulk. When a suspended ceiling is used, the vapour from the stored cargo is contained by the outer wall. However, this outer wall is not designed to contain the liquid cargo. In-tank pumps with piping exiting through the tank roof were installed to maintain the tank wall integrity.

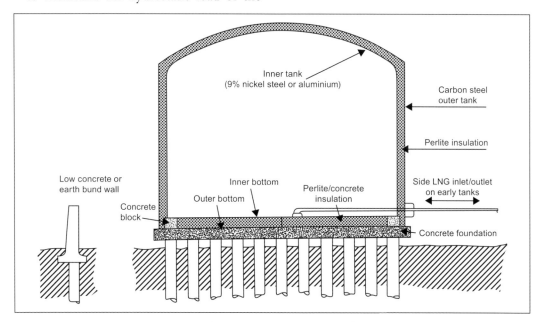

Figure 8.3 Single Containment LNG Tank. (SIGTTO.)

101

This type of tank presents minimal protection against external hazards such as fire, impact, etc. In case of leak or failure, the stored product is released to atmosphere and a low bund wall would be erected to prevent uncontrolled liquid spillage.

This type of tank has been widely used for LPG, ethylene and LNG. It is still popular in the United States.

b) ***Double Containment*** – A double containment tank consists of:

- The same inner tank as the single containment design but with a tight roof.

- Insulation around the inner tank, either polyurethane foam with a vapour barrier or perlite in bulk enclosed in a carbon steel outer shell.

- An outer tank designed to contain any liquid in case of failure of the inner tank, but not designed to contain the vapour. The outer tank must be no further than 6 meters from the inner tank.

- A weather cover may be provided between tank roof and outer wall and a return water pump must be provided if a deluge system is fitted.

- The inner tank may be 9% nickel steel, stainless steel membrane or aluminium. The outer tank is generally pre-stressed concrete but may also be 9% nickel steel.

- Submerged pumps are provided in-tank with discharge piping through the tank roof.

- The tank base will be in direct contact with the ground, so a base heating system is required.

A few of these tanks have been used for LNG application. They are very similar to the single containment type, except for the added security of being able to contain the cargo liquid within the second containment in case of failure of the first containment. In such a case, however, the vapour is left to escape to the outside.

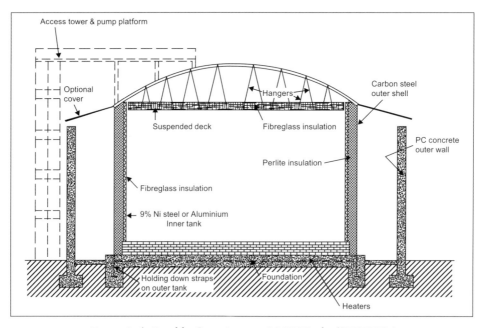

Figure 8.4 Double Containment LNG Tank. (SIGTTO.)

c) ***Full Containment*** – Tanks known as "Full Containment" or "Double Integrity" are made up of two tanks both designed to contain the stored product fully. In normal operation the product is contained in the inner tank, made of material adapted to the minimum temperature of the stored product and similar to the single wall tank. The outer container is a pre-stressed concrete tank designed to contain the stored product fully in case of failure of the inner tank. The outer tank can also be made of low temperature steel. The insulation material, placed between the two tanks can be either polyurethane foam or perlite in bulk on the vertical wall and glass foam on the bottom.

All piping and instrumentation are directed through the tank roof and a base heating system is required.

This type of tank has been in general use in recent years. It provides good protection against deterioration due to atmospheric causes, external damage by fire or impact and failure of the inner tank. It can be used above-ground, semi-buried or in-ground.

d) ***Membrane Tanks*** – The membrane tanks described in part 8.4.1.**b)** "In-Ground tanks" are of the double integrity or full containment type. All in-ground tanks are membrane tanks, but membrane tanks can also be installed above-ground or semi-buried, when the outer shell of the tank is made in pre-stressed concrete. They are quite expensive to build and are used mainly for LNG. A simpler version has been put forward for products having a minimum storage temperature of –55°C, such as butane, propane, butadiene or propylene. The principle is the same as for the membrane type but the expensive membrane is replaced by a liquid and gastight cryogenic liner called Triplex, bonded to the insulation. Triplex is an aluminium foil held between two layers of glass cloth. This type of construction is obviously cheaper than the conventional membrane.

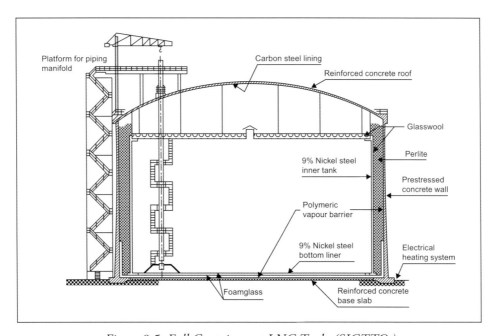

Figure 8.5 Full Containment LNG Tank. (SIGTTO.)

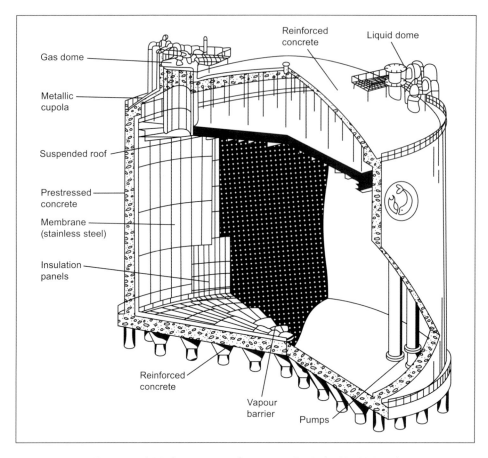

Figure 8.6 Technigaz Membrane LNG Tank. (SIGTTO.)

72. A Technigaz Membrane LNG Tank. (GTT.)

8.4.3 STANDARD FOR LOW TEMPERATURE CYLINDRICAL VERTICAL STORAGE TANKS

There are two main internationally recognised standards for low temperature vertical storage tanks, API 620 (appendix Q) and BS 7777. A European Standard is in the process of being formulated.

i)   American Petroleum Institute API 620 – This Standard did not originally address low temperature tanks. Two appendices have been added, giving recommendations for these tanks. Appendix R covers tanks for products with a minimum temperature of –50°C and appendix Q, products with a minimum temperature of –196°C. The Standard does not specify special requirements for double or full containment tanks.

ii) British Standard BS 7777 – This Standard, published in 1993, was specifically developed for low temperature storage. It has superseded BS 5387. BS 7777 is the only standard to identify Single, Double and Full containment systems. Due to the difference in the type of hydraulic test applied, the thickness of the steel plates required by the BS for tanks containing low density products, such as LNG, is greater than that required by the API Standard. Due to the limitation in welding technology for 9% nickel steel, the BS does not allow the construction of tanks above a certain size in this material.

8.4.4 MATERIALS USED FOR LOW TEMPERATURE STORAGE TANKS

The material of construction for refrigerated tanks depends on the storage temperature. Carbon steels, in some cases nickel alloy steels or even composite materials, are used for LPG and chemical gases where the minimum temperature remains above –55°C. For products such as ethylene or LNG with much lower temperatures, alternative materials, 9% nickel steel, austenitic stainless steel, Invar or aluminium alloy must be used.

An increasing concern for safety has resulted in the more general use of double containment tanks or even double integrity systems for liquefied gas. This has developed the use of prestressed concrete which is now very much in favour, especially for LNG tanks.

The foundations of refrigerated tanks, particularly those built for holding LNG, require specialised attention. The tank foundations must be carefully designed to avoid possible settlement and a reliable heating system is necessary to prevent the ground freezing, leading to frost heave conditions.

Protection of the insulation against ingress of moisture was a concern with the earlier tanks but with the generalisation of double containment, this problem is now resolved.

8.5 EVOLUTION OF THE SIZE OF SHORE STORAGE TANKS

The capacity of the first tanks built in the 1940's was in the order of 2,000 m³ and this gradually increased to 5, 000 m³. These tanks were single containment, spherical or horizontal cylindrical. Those for LNG were used for peak-shaving storage.

The beginning of the 1960's saw the start of the vertical cylindrical tanks for LNG and LPG. Capacities were still below 10,000 m³. These tanks were single containment, built in aluminium/carbon steel with bottom outlet and a low bund wall.

Size increased to 45,000 m³ at the beginning of the 1970's and to 60,000 m³ in the mid 1970's. The bottom outlet disappeared and double containment, full containment and underground tanks were introduced.

Size continued to increase and the first underground membrane tank, with a capacity of 200,000 m³, was commissioned in 1998.

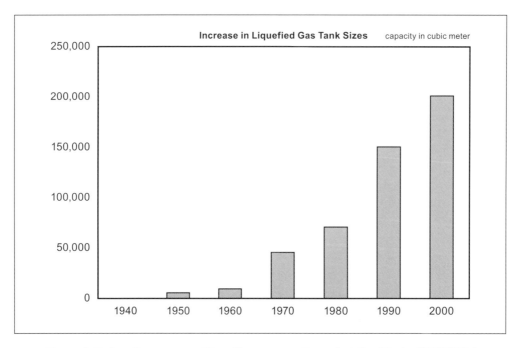

Figure 8.7 Size Progression of Low Temperature Liquefied Gas Tank. (SIGTTO.)

73. Various Above Ground Tanks. (SIGTTO.)

8.6 SOME POSSIBLE INCIDENTS IN LIQUEFIED GAS SHORE STORAGE TANKS

8.6.1 ROLLOVER

The expression "rollover" was first used to describe strange happenings observed in some lakes where, at certain times of the year, the water suddenly becomes disturbed and mud and debris from the bottom suddenly appear on the surface. This is caused by changes in the water density due to variations in the atmospheric temperature.

Liquefied gas stored in a tank at almost atmospheric pressure and low boiling temperature gains heat from outside through the imperfect insulation and this causes the product to boil off. Usually the product located at the top of the tank boils off faster than the product at the bottom and this can eventually create layers of liquid with different relative densities. In LPG tanks, the boil-off gas is reliquefied and returned into the tank, creating a certain movement in the liquid which is sufficient to ensure a good mix. In LNG tanks, however, the boil-off is used outside the tank. Under normal conditions, currents circulate from tank bottom to tank top and the density of the product inside remains homogeneous; however, this is not always sufficient to maintain a good balance. If the tank contains two or more layers of LNG of differing densities, the interface between them prevents the convection currents circulating and the boil-off stops in the lower part of the tank, which only aggravates the situation. The difference in density between top and bottom continues to increase and there is a serious risk that, at some time, the position of the two liquids will reverse suddenly, resulting in a spontaneous rapid mixing of the layers, accompanied by a violent vapour generation. The result of this phenomenon in a large tank can be quite dramatic, with a sudden rise in pressure inside the tank and the release of a large amount of vapour through the venting system. If the venting system is not able to cope with the surge of vapour, it is possible for the tank to incur damage.

Rollover is a particular risk in peak-shaving plants, where liquid is stored for long periods of time. Import terminals may also face this problem when two products from different suppliers are mixed into one tank.

Rollover is preventable by good tank management. Tank content must be monitored for temperature gradient, density and boil-off rate. At the first sign of abnormality, the contents of the tank should be circulated to stop the problem developing further.

8.6.2 FIRE HAZARD

The main hazard in a shore storage plant is fire. Fire can result from a leaking product, liquid or vapour, if it is ignited on the site; it can be caused by a mechanical incident or human error; or it can occur on a neighbouring industrial site. Fire can damage the other tanks by impingement, reducing the mechanical property of the tank material or by radiation, increasing the internal pressure, or a combination of the two. This is why in-ground or mounded tanks are more able to resist a fire without damage. It is also the reason all above-ground tanks should be protected by a deluge system.

A few terminal accidents have resulted in a lot of damage, for example in Mexico City and in Feysin, France. In these cases, the fire, once started, created a chain reaction, damaging the other tanks one after another, with very harmful effects. In Mexico, a number of pressurised horizontal cylindrical tanks were damaged and acted like missiles being projected several hundred metres.

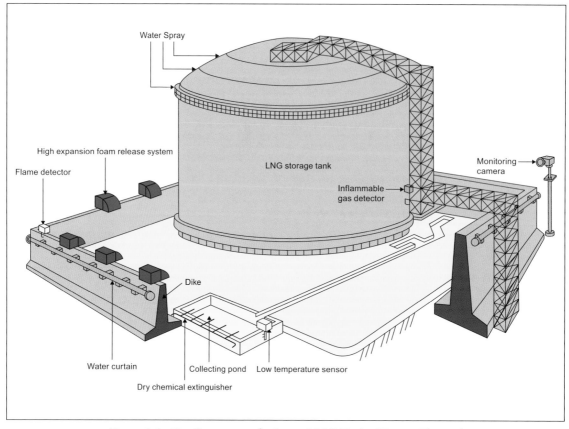

Figure 8.8 Fire Protection of a Large LNG Tank. (Kansai Electric.)

This is one of the reasons why those tanks must now be mounded. Pressurised spherical tanks were subjected to the very frightening BLEVE effect which will be described later. Fortunately, such accidents are rare but these resulted in many fatalities, not only in the plant but also among the surrounding population.

Leak prevention, fire prevention and fire protection are essential elements of storage terminal safety which must be scrupulously evaluated and maintained. Contingency plans must be ready in case of emergency and terminal personnel need to be thoroughly trained and fully familiar with the implementation of these plans.

8.6.3 BOILING LIQUID EXPANDING VAPOUR EXPLOSION (BLEVE)

If a pressurised tank is exposed to fire radiation without any protection, the pressure inside can rise well above the level for which the tank was designed and, at the same time, flame impingement can diminish the mechanical resistance of the tank envelope. In such a case, there is a possibility of the tank envelope tearing open and releasing its contents in the middle of the existing fire, with disastrous consequences. This is a very frightening phenomenon and it has spectacular results. Unfortunately, when it happens in the middle of a real fire, it also has very damaging effects.

74. *Boiling Liquid Expanding Vapour Explosion (BLEVE). (Canadian Coast Guard.)*

Chapter 9
OPERATIONS

9.1 SHIP OPERATIONS

9.1.1 GENERAL

There is no major difference between the general operation of a liquefied gas tanker and the operation of any other type of ship. Before going to sea, a ship must be in good operating condition and seaworthy and the crew must be adequately trained in its operation and maintenance. In Chapter 6, we have seen that there are international rules controlling this and these rules apply to all ships.

However, in view of the hazardous cargo transported by a liquefied gas tanker, the crew must be trained to be extra vigilant and to consider at all times the potential risk under which the ship, its crew and its cargo is placed.

Liquefied gas tanker crews must be trained specifically in the following subjects:

- Characteristics of the different products carried by their ship.

- Precautions to be taken for the safety of personnel in case of cargo escape.

- Cargo handling and cargo operations.

- Fire-fighting, in particular the specific aspect of fire protection for the products carried.

- Contingency planning for the various catastrophic situations which could confront the crew [12.13].

There should be no need for extra navigation training, although emphasis must be put on maintaining a reasonable and prudent attitude at all times and avoiding any possibility of grounding or collision, which could endanger the integrity of the cargo containment of their vessel.

Frequent multinational crews make a common language, understood by all crew members, essential and it is imperative that all training is conducted in this language.

9.1.2 CARGO OPERATIONS

The characteristics of the different cargoes transported and the specific requirements for their safe transport are what make liquefied gas tankers different from other ships.

The international regulations listed in Chapter 6 require that crews and officers manning liquefied gas tankers obtain certificates confirming their successful attendance at specific training sessions. These training sessions must cover the characteristics of the products transported and the precautions to be taken in case of release to atmosphere of these products. This should include the first-aid treatments required in case of exposure to toxic or cryogenic products. The officers must also be trained in the operation of all the specialised equipment used on board for cargo handling and monitoring.

The full sequence of cargo operations on a liquefied gas tanker, from the delivery of the ship at the end of construction or at the end of drydocking until the next drydocking, can be separated into a number of sections which have to be carried out once or several times during the period.

- Preparation for loading
- Loading
- Loaded voyage
- Discharge
- Ballast voyage
- Changing cargo Preparation for drydocking

a) *Preparation for loading*

The tanks of a liquefied gas tanker just delivered from the shipyard at the end of construction or at the end of a drydock period are usually open and under air atmosphere. When the tanks are open to the atmosphere, they should always be kept in a dry condition by circulating dry air, to avoid any possibility of corrosion.

Prior to closing the tanks, a very thorough inspection must be carried out. All parts must be perfectly clean and dry, all loose objects must be removed and all fittings secured, with stoppers in place. Pumps must be checked for free rotation and valves for free operation. The tanks can then be closed, using new gaskets.

Once the tanks are closed, all water vapour and free water must be removed from the cargo system. Even if the tanks were kept dry whilst open, they are certainly not dry enough to receive cargo. Any moisture remaining could cause icing due to the low temperature of the cargo. Some products can react in the presence of water to produce hydrates which clog filters and freeze valves and pumps.

Drying of tank atmosphere can be achieved by various means:

- Using dry air produced on board. This dry air can be produced using the inert gas generator blower and dryer but without firing the burner. This procedure is used if sufficient time is available. It reduces the

amount of inert gas to be used later for the inerting operation but takes more time than drying at the same time as inerting.

- Using inert gas from shore as part of the inerting procedure. This method reduces the moisture content in the atmosphere down to the required dew point and at the same time reduces the oxygen content. This is done in case of LNG, ethylene or a product requiring an atmosphere with very low oxygen content such as butadiene or VCM or in the case of ammonia which reacts with the carbon dioxide of the inert gas produced on board.

- Using inert gas from the on-board generator. This follows the same principle as when the inert gas is supplied from shore. The inert gas production must be carefully monitored for good quality and a low dew point.

Whichever way the drying operation is carried out, it must be conducted until a dew-point of at least −40°C is obtained.

The next stage of the tank preparation is the inerting operation and we have seen that, when time is short, drying and inerting can be done at the same time.

Chapter 6.3.5 describes how inert gas is obtained on board. Inerting cargo tanks, cargo machinery and piping is carried out to ensure a non-flammable condition when first introducing cargo vapour into the system for the gassing-up operation. To achieve this, the oxygen content must be reduced from 21% to a maximum of 5% by volume. The theory shows that a mixture of hydrocarbon gas and air is non-flammable when the oxygen content is less than 10 to 12%. However the maximum value of 5% is used on gas carriers, to allow for a degree of poor mixing in the tank. Another reason for reducing the oxygen content prior to introducing cargo into the tank is that some products react chemically with a very small quantity of oxygen. In the case of butadiene or VCM, oxygen content as low as 0.1% is necessary to avoid such a reaction. In these cases, inert gas must be taken from shore as the on-board system can only produce inert gas with an oxygen content approaching 0.5%.

There are several ways to conduct the inerting operation:

• For a type C tank, it is possible to use the dilution system. This type of tank can sustain a considerable vacuum, in the range of 30 to 70 per cent depending on the design and can also be pressurised to quite a high level. The operation consists in drawing the maximum possible vacuum into the tanks with the ship's compressors

and then injecting the inert gas up to a pressure of two or three bar. The pressure is then released and the operation repeated until the required oxygen level and dew point are obtained. This is a very efficient way to inert this type of tank without using too much inert gas.

• For tanks of A, B and membrane types which are not designed to sustain any significant pressure, the only possible way would be continuous dilution. However, this would take a long time and would use far too much inert gas. Fortunately, it is possible to take advantage of the slight difference in density existing between air and inert gas and to use what is currently called the piston effect. Inert gas is slightly heavier than air and, if introduced in a

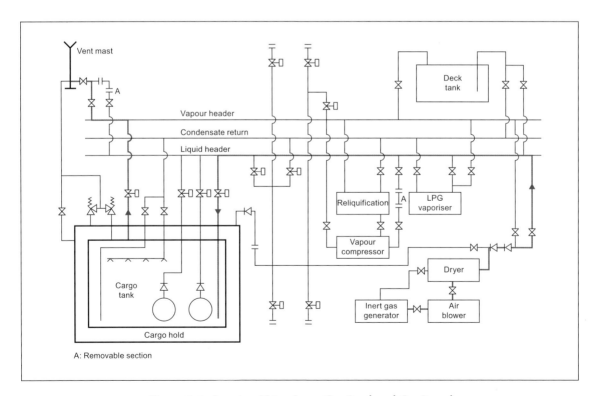

Figure 9.1 Inerting Using Inert-Gas Produced On Board.

113

regular flow at the bottom of the tank, it will stay at the bottom and push air up without too much mixing of the two. If the flow of inert gas is kept constant, without surge, the tank will gradually fill up with inert gas and the air will be removed to the venting mast through the vapour line at the top of the tank. This operation will usually take an amount of inert gas equivalent to two or two and a half times the volume of the tanks and lasts about 12 hours. If the ship's inert gas generator can produce a sufficient amount of inert gas, the flow can be spread between all the tanks. This is called "inerting the tanks in parallel". If, however, the inert gas production is too low, providing the ship's piping allows it, the full flow of inert gas can be sent to the bottom of one tank and the air exiting this tank can be sent to the bottom of the next tank. The discharge of the second tank will be sent to the bottom of the third and so on through all the tanks. This can save some time and some quantity of inert gas. It is called "inerting the tanks in series".

The method to be used for inerting has to be selected according to the ship type and particular design. Whichever method is used, it is important to monitor the oxygen concentration and the dew point from time to time in the different tanks, using the sampling connections provided at different heights in each tank. It is also important, before completing the inerting operation, to ensure that no oxygen-rich atmosphere remains in any of the piping or machinery equipment. When the tank atmosphere has reached the required oxygen level, it is good practice to raise the inert gas pressure in each tank to just below the relief valve setting point. This will confirm that the tank cover is not leaking and that the relief valves are set correctly. The pressure available can be used to blow through all the

cargo piping and machinery equipment, pushing out any remaining air.

The hold space around the tanks must also be in the appropriate condition to be ready to load cargo. Most of the LPG ships maintain those spaces under dry air, to avoid any condensation. The hold spaces or insulation spaces on LNG ships are kept under CO_2 free inert gas.

The last operation to be conducted prior to loading cargo is the gassing-up. It consists of replacing the inert gas in the tanks with vapour of the cargo to be loaded, at ambient temperature. The different procedures to be used are similar to those described above for the replacement of air by inert gas, taking advantage of the difference in density between the vapour to be used and the inert gas. Most hydrocarbon gas vapour is heavier than inert gas at ambient temperature, except for methane and ethylene. This operation is necessary on LPG ships as neither nitrogen nor carbon dioxide, the main constituents of inert gas, can be condensed by a ship's reliquefaction plant. At cargo temperature, they both are above their critical temperatures and are therefore incondensible and it is necessary to remove them from the system prior to starting the reliquefaction plant. On LNG ships, if the inerting has been done using inert gas produced on board, the gassing-up operation is also necessary because carbon dioxide freezes at $-56.6°C$ which is well above $-162°C$, the loading temperature of LNG. If the inerting operation has been carried out with shore supplied nitrogen containing no carbon dioxide, however, the gassing-up operation is not required and the tanks can be cooled down directly.

Some ships are equipped with pressurised deck tanks in which different products can be kept. If one tank contains a sufficient quantity of the appropriate product, the gassing-up operation can be conducted at sea and the mixture of inert gas and product vapour discharged into the atmosphere. Otherwise the operation must be carried out in the loading terminal. Either the shore can supply vapour directly to the ship or, if this is not possible, a small flow of liquid is sent to the ship's vaporiser where it is vaporised before being directed to the ship's tanks. As it is not possible to discharge a mixture of inert gas and hydrocarbon gas to atmosphere in port, the terminal must be equipped to receive what is discharged from the ship and dispose of it in a suitable way. Most of the time it is sent to a flare, where the inert gas is vented and any hydrocarbon vapours are burnt. Prior to connecting the ship's manifold to the terminal system and receiving vapour from the ship, the terminal will conduct a thorough survey of the ship's tanks to ensure that they contain only inert gas. The quantity of vapour or liquid supplied by the terminal to the ship must also be carefully measured for future

invoicing. When the content of product to be loaded reaches approximately 90 per cent of the tanks' atmosphere, the flow can be sent to the ship's reliquefaction plant and the discharge ashore closed. The cool-down operation can then be started.

b) *Loading*

Prior to loading a refrigerated cargo, the ship's tanks must be cooled down slowly. This is necessary to minimise thermal stresses and to avoid an excessive rise in tank pressure due to flash evaporation during bulk loading. The rate of cool-down depends on the design of the containment system and on the cargo carriage temperature, but a typical figure is 10°C per hour.

A normal cool-down procedure is to introduce a small flow of cargo liquid, received from shore, into the tanks through spray lines, if specially

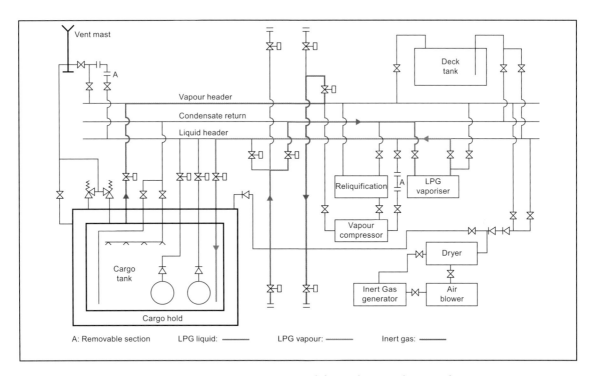

Figure 9.2 Gassing-Up Using Liquid from Shore in the case of LPG.

fitted, or through the loading line. The vapour produced by the rapid evaporation may be taken ashore or handled by the ship's reliquefaction plant. This operation is continued at a rate corresponding to the cool-down rate required. The ship's cargo operation manual gives all indications on the rate of cool-down and the temperature required to be achieved for each different product to be loaded. In the case of LNG, for example, the cool-down operation will take approximately 12 hours, as a very low temperature must be reached. During cool-down, the reduction of the temperature in the tanks will cause them to contract and also induce a drop of temperature in the space around the tanks. The pressure in these spaces must be controlled as it, too, will drop and it should be ensured that the pressure control system operates correctly. This is especially important on membrane-type ships as a substantial make-up of nitrogen is required

during the cool-down operation to maintain positive pressure in the insulation space.

Cool-down should continue until boil-off eases and liquid starts to accumulate at the bottom of the tanks. This can be confirmed from the temperature sensors located at the bottom of the tanks. The temperature at the top of the tank will still be much higher than at the bottom. Indications of acceptable temperature differences between tank top and bottom prior to the start of bulk loading are available from the cargo operating manual. In the case of LPG, some difficulty may be encountered during the cool-down operation, with icing or hydrate formation. This can be alleviated by introducing antifreeze, if this is allowed by the cargo specification. During the cool-down operation, the pump shafts must be regularly turned by hand to prevent the pumps freezing up. The cargo pipelines must also be cooled at the same time.

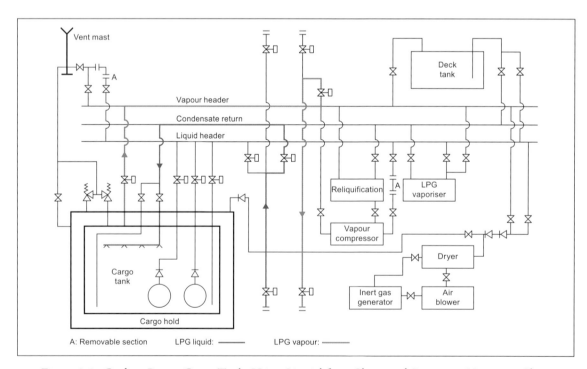

Figure 9.3 Cooling Down Cargo Tanks Using Liquid from Shore and Returning Vapour to Shore.

All pre-operational ship/shore procedures, as described in the next chapter, must have been thoroughly discussed with the terminal, prior to starting the cool-down operation. The ship's personnel must ensure that they have all the necessary information on the cargo to be loaded, the procedures to be followed by the terminal for the loading operation, the procedures to be followed in case of emergency and on how to maintain open communications with the terminal at all times. They must have checked the following points:

- Tank safety valves, high pressure and high level alarms set at the correct values.

- The ship will have the required trim and stability conditions at the end of loading.

- Deballasting can be conducted concurrently with the loading operation.

- Maximum pressure and flow, minimum temperature, and disposal of boil-off have all been agreed with the terminal.

- The Emergency Shut-Down links between ship and shore are installed and the system checked for good operation.

- If the ship is arriving to load with some cargo from the previous voyage remaining in the tanks, the level of this cargo must be carefully measured and its quantity calculated.

Once all these checks are confirmed, the bulk loading operation can start. It is usual to start slowly, the speed gradually increasing up to the flow agreed with the terminal. If a vapour return line to shore is used, the flow must be confirmed as acceptable by the terminal. If the vapour displaced by the loaded liquid and the boil-off resulting from the energy injected into the cargo through friction in pumps and piping are reliquefied on board, the loading rate must

75. LPG Tanker at a Loading Berth.

be adjusted to correspond to the performance of the reliquefaction plant. At the start of the loading operation, careful checks must be made on board to ensure that the piping circuit is correctly organised and that all liquid coming from shore goes into the tanks. Throughout loading, frequent checks must be made of the tank levels, pressures and temperatures. Pressures and temperatures must also be checked in the spaces around the tank to ensure that all is normal. Ballasting and bunkering, if carried out at the same time, must be carefully supervised to maintain the ship in trim and not subject the hull to any overstress. As loading reaches completion, tanks must be brought to their maximum level one by one and the terminal given sufficient notice to be able to slow down and stop without causing an overflow.

The maximum loading level for each tank is specified by the IMO Gas Code. It depends on the maximum pressure allowed in the tank, the product loaded and the atmospheric conditions during the voyage. This is to avoid the possibility that, in case of a fire, the tanks will ever be overfilled. The reverse situation when, starting with a low level of loaded product, the quantity of liquid in the tank is further reduced by over vaporisation, leaving the tank walls vulnerable to flame impingement without the cooling protection afforded by the liquid, is equally dangerous and must also be avoided.

After completion of loading, the terminal and the ship will proceed together with the purging of the shore loading arms or hoses prior to their disconnection, to avoid any release of cargo. Once purging is complete, disconnection can take place.

On termination of loading, tank levels must be carefully checked and the quantity of cargo loaded calculated, usually with the assistance of a surveyor representing the interests of the Charterer.

The ship can then leave the terminal and proceed to sea.

There can be variations on the loading operation described above: loading a pressurised ship from a pressurised storage or loading a pressurised ship from a fully refrigerated storage through a cargo heater or loading a cargo at ambient temperature into a fully refrigerated ship with refrigeration during loading. All these operations will, in essence, be conducted as the one detailed above and it would be too lengthy to describe here the technical details involved.

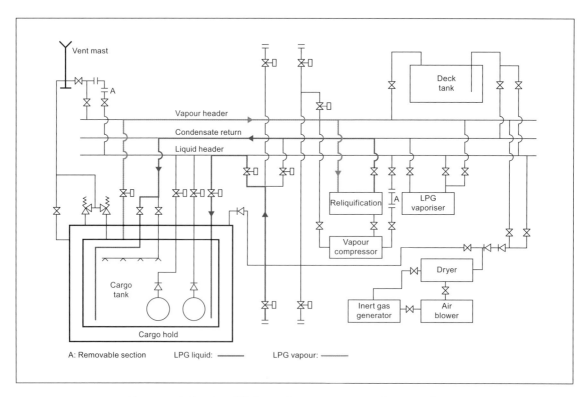

Figure 9.4 Loading Without Vapour Return in the case of LPG.

c) *Loaded Voyage*

During the loaded voyage of a semi-pressurised or fully-refrigerated ship, the reliquefaction plant must be operated as necessary to maintain the cargo temperatures and pressures within the prescribed limits. On most modern ships, this is done by measuring the tank pressures and starting and stopping the plant automatically for a specified pressure window. If the reliquefaction plant is operated on several tanks in parallel, it is necessary to ensure that the condensate returns are spread equally between each tank. If the cargo temperature has to be reduced during the voyage, it is better to run the reliquefaction plant non-stop at the beginning of the voyage until the required temperature is reached, rather than wait until the last days of the voyage.

On a pressurised ship, the tanks are kept closed and the only control is, when in very warm areas, to ensure that the temperature does not rise above the estimated value for the voyage, taking the liquid level above the prescribed limits. Should this happen, the spray water system would have to be started to reduce the tank temperature.

On LNG ships, the boil-off is used in the ship's boiler and the compressors automatically control the tank pressures. The boiler control management adjusts the amount of fuel oil and the amount of boil-off available to produce the amount of steam required.

Throughout the loaded voyage, regular checks must be made to ensure that there is no malfunction in the cargo equipment and no

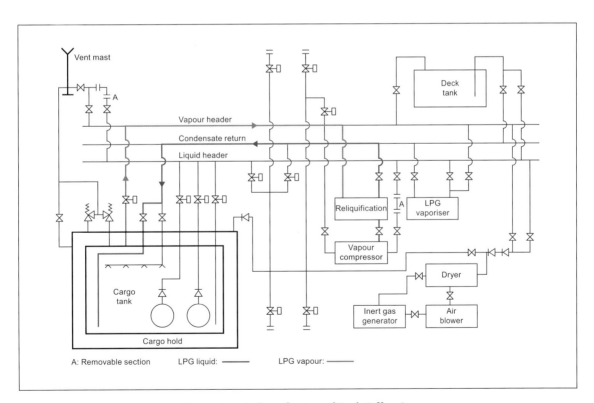

Figure 9.5 Reliquefaction of Boil-Off at Sea.

leaks in the nitrogen or air supply lines. On LNG ships, visual cold-spot inspections should be carried out in the cargo tank surrounds, even if the ships are fitted with temperature monitoring of the inner hull surfaces. In carrying out these inspections, all relevant safety procedures for entry into enclosed spaces must be adhered to and due regard given to hazardous atmospheres in adjacent spaces. On Membrane ships, the operation of the pressure control system for the interbarrier spaces must be checked regularly.

d) *Discharging*

When a ship arrives at the discharge terminal, cargo tank pressures and temperatures should be in accordance with the terminal requirements and all cargo equipment should be in good operating condition. The ESD system and the main pumps and valves must have been checked for good operation the day before arrival.

Any discrepancy must be brought to the attention of the terminal management prior to the ship's arrival. Similarly, the terminal must advise the ship of any problem with the terminal equipment.

Before the discharging operation begins, the pre-operational ship/shore procedures should be carried out in the same way as for the loading operation. The level in the cargo tanks must be carefully measured and the quantity of cargo on arrival must be carefully calculated, if necessary with the assistance of a surveyor.

After connecting the shore piping and the ESD links, testing the connections under pressure and the ESD system for good operation, the cool-down of the piping can start.

Discharging can be carried out by different methods depending on the type of ship, cargo specification and terminal storage.

- Discharge by pressurising the vapour space: this is done on pressurised ships

with type C tanks. It is sometimes helped by a booster pump.

- Discharge with deepwell or submerged pumps: the number of pumps to be used will depend on the number of tanks to be discharged and on the flow which can be accepted by the terminal. In some cases, when the pressure required to reach the shore tanks is higher than the discharge pressure of the ship's deepwell or submerged pumps, a booster pump may be used. The operation of the pumps has to be monitored throughout the discharge so as to maintain a constant discharge pressure. When the liquid level goes down in the tank, the discharge valve of the pumps will need to be throttled, with a corresponding reduction of flow. This is particularly important at the end of discharge, if it is necessary to leave the tanks with a level as low as possible. When the refrigerated cargo on the ship is to be discharged into a storage at ambient temperature, it is necessary to use a booster pump and a cargo heater. The speed of discharge will have to be adjusted to the performance of the cargo heater.

Whichever method is used to discharge the cargo, the liquid level in the cargo tanks should be carefully monitored, bearing in mind ship stability and hull stress. Ballasting operations will have to be carried out to maintain a suitable trim and keep the ship's hull within acceptable structural stress limits. Removal of liquid from the cargo tank may cause changes in inter-barrier space pressures and these should be monitored throughout the discharge operation. The boil-off due to the heat flow through the tank insulation is usually insufficient to maintain the tank pressure, which is falling because of the liquid being pumped out. This will obviously depend on the discharge rate, but for a normal discharge

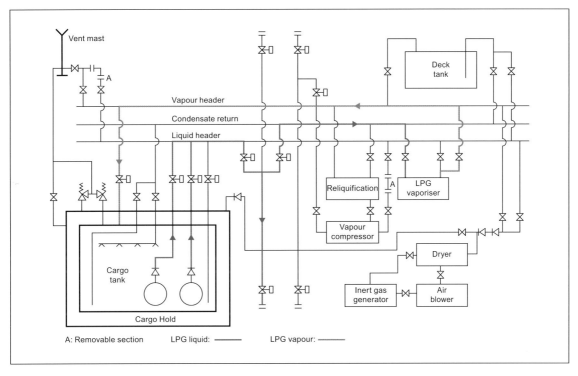

Vent mast
Deck tank
Vapour header
Condensate return
Liquid header
A
Reliquification
LPG vaporiser
Vapour compressor
Dryer
Cargo tank
Inert gas generator
Air blower
Cargo Hold

A: Removable section   LPG liquid: ———   LPG vapour: ———

Figure 9.6 Discharging without Vapour Return.

it is necessary to add vapour to the tanks to maintain the discharge rate. This can be done through a vapour return line from shore or by diverting some of the liquid being discharged through the ship's vaporiser.

After completion of discharge, the sequence of operations is the same as at the end of loading: pipe drainage, disconnection, calculation of quantity of remaining liquid and vapour. The quantity of cargo discharged is obtained by subtracting the quantity remaining at the end of discharge from the quantity on board on arrival.

e) *Ballast Voyage*

Refrigerated ships returning to load the same product usually retain a small quantity of the cargo on board after discharge. This is called the heel and is used to maintain the tanks at reduced temperature during the ballast voyage. The quantity retained on board will depend on the type of ship, type of cargo and the duration of the voyage. It will also depend on the commercial agreements with the charterer. On LPG ships, the amount kept on board should be sufficient to run the reliquefaction plant from time to time, returning the condensate to the tanks to ensure arrival at the loading terminal with tanks ready to load. On LNG ships with tanks of the membrane type, it is only necessary to keep enough cargo to ensure that, on arrival at the loading port, there will still be some liquid at the bottom of the tanks. In these tanks, the temperature at the top of the tank will stay around –65°C without the need for any circulation, so long as there is liquid at the tank bottom. On ships with type B tanks, it is necessary to keep a slightly larger quantity of cargo, sufficient to ensure that the spray pumps are still able to circulate cargo at the end of the voyage. As the weight of tank material is much higher in type B tanks than in membrane-type tanks, it is necessary to maintain the temperature all around the tank by circulating liquid with small submerged cool-down or spray pumps installed at the bottom of the tanks, through spray nozzles fitted at the top.

If the ship is due to load a different cargo from the one just discharged, none of the previous cargo should be retained on board. If the ship is fitted with deck tanks, the remaining amount, which cannot be pumped out, can be stored in an available deck tank. Otherwise all cargo must be vented off and the tanks prepared for the next cargo.

f) *Changing Cargo or Preparation for Dry docking*

This is probably the most time-consuming part of a liquefied gas carrier operation. If the next cargo is not compatible with the previous one, a visual inspection of the tanks is often imposed by the charterer, which would require the tanks to be gas free. This is usually the case when loading chemical gases, such as vinyl chloride, butadiene or ethylene. It is also the case when the previous cargo was ammonia. Guidance on the compatibility of different cargoes is usually given in the ship's operation manual and this has to be checked to know what preparation is necessary prior to arriving at the loading port, if the information is not given by the charterer.

The following operations have to be carried out to obtain a gas-free condition:

- Removal of remaining liquid
- Warm-up the tanks
- Inert the tanks
- Aerate the tanks

This sequence of operations is the same in case of tank entry for visual inspection or to prepare the ship for drydock.

If the operations are carried out while the ship is at sea, the remaining liquid and vapour will be vented out to the atmosphere or, if a deck tank is available, stored in the deck tank, using the reliquefaction plant. If the operation is carried out in port, either at a gas-freeing berth or at the loading terminal, the remaining liquid and vapour must be disposed of to a flare or to a vapour recovery system, if one is available.

In case of pressurised or semi-pressurised tanks, the remaining liquid can be removed by pressurisation if the liquid can be easily disposed of. Otherwise it is necessary to vaporise the remaining liquid. Most modern LPG ships are fitted with heating coils in the cargo pump sumps. Warm vapour is circulated through the heating coil to vaporise the liquid remaining in the sumps. On ships not equipped with heating coils or on LNG ships, vaporising the remaining liquid and warming up the tanks is done at the same time by using the compressors to circulate warm vapour through the bottom of the tanks. The vapour is returned to the compressors from the top of the tanks and the circulation is maintained until the temperature at the bottom of the tanks is higher than the condensing temperature of the heaviest component of the product. When warming up an LNG tank, for example, as LNG contains, among other things, a small amount of butane (C_4H_{10}), it is necessary to have temperatures at the tank bottom well above 0°C before stopping the warming-up operation, to be sure that all liquid is vaporised.

When the tanks are free of liquid and warmed to a temperature higher than the dew point of the gas to be used for inerting, the inerting operation can be started. The reason for continuing the warm-up to such a temperature is to avoid any possibility of condensation when the inert gas is introduced. The inerting operation is conducted as explained earlier in the Chapter a) "Preparation Before Loading", taking advantage of the difference of density between the inert gas and the vapour remaining in the tanks. If inerting is carried out prior to loading the next cargo and if a visual inspection of the tanks is not required, the operation can be stopped when the content of the last cargo in the tank atmosphere is below the figure recommended for loading the next cargo. The tanks can then be gassed-up with vapour of the next cargo. If inerting is carried out prior to opening the tanks, the operation can be stopped when there remains less of the last cargo than the figure recommended by the shipyard receiving the ship or by the inspector due to carry out the inspection. A figure of 0.5%, or sometimes even 0.2%, is usually recommended. The tanks can then be aerated until obtaining an oxygen content of 21%, prior to being opened and entered for inspection.

g) *Changing Cargo after Ammonia.*

This is a very delicate and long operation. Ammonia reacts with the carbon dioxide contained in the inert gas produced on board. It is also extremely miscible in water. Finally the maximum amount of ammonia accepted in the tank atmosphere prior to loading a cargo of LPG or chemical gases is 20 ppm by volume or 0.002%. Many charterers even refuse to load LPG on ships having just completed an ammonia voyage. They insist on a minimum of three cargoes after the last ammonia cargo. Cleaning tanks after ammonia must be conducted very carefully. It is very important to maintain a dry atmosphere in the tanks throughout the operation If the slightest amount of condensation occurs in the tanks while some ammonia vapour is still present, the ammonia will be absorbed by the water and this can mix with any small amount of rust or

dust inside the tanks and become very difficult to eliminate. Due to the difficulty of disposing of ammonia vapour ashore, the operation is usually carried out at sea, venting the tanks directly with air. The tanks must be liquid-free and warmed up to a temperature well above the ambient temperature. They must be vented with air as dry as possible and the venting operation must be continued until the ammonia content in all tanks, piping and cargo machinery is below 200 ppm. The tanks must then be opened and entered for sweeping out all loose material present which could trap ammonia vapour. Obviously, all necessary safety precautions must be taken when entering the tanks and breathing aids must be used if at all necessary. Ventilation must be continued throughout this operation and maintained until ammonia content in the tank's atmosphere is below 20 ppm. The whole operation will probably take more than a week.

76. Ship Centralised Control Room.

9.2 PORT OPERATIONS

9.2.1 GENERAL

The previous chapter has described ship operations. In this chapter, it is the turn of the port and terminal operations to be reviewed. This will be done, looking at a ship arriving at a port and berthing at a terminal to load or discharge its cargo and then depart.

9.2.2 EXCHANGE OF INFORMATION BETWEEN SHIP, PORT AND TERMINAL

In Chapter 7.3 we have seen the importance of the pre-arrival exchange of information between ship, port and terminal. The port authority and the terminal management must have received the characteristics of the arriving ship in advance to ensure that it can be accommodated by their facilities. They must ensure that the rules and regulations of the port and terminal have been communicated to the ship. They must ascertain that the ship is in good operating condition and that all equipment likely to be used while the ship is in the port or terminal is in working order. They must ensure that the crew speaks a language understood by the terminal personnel or that an interpreter will be available. They must also ensure that the ship is aware of the characteristics of the products to be transferred and that there is not, on board, any other product incompatible with these products or liable to create a dangerous situation while the ship is in the terminal.

In the case of an LNG project having several ships visiting one terminal at regular intervals over several years, meetings between the ship's management, port authorities and the terminal management can start more than a year before the first arrival of the first ship and continue regularly throughout the life of the project. LPG ships visit many different terminals, sometimes at short notice, but it should still be possible to obtain the required information before the ship's arrival.

Based on the Estimated Time of Arrival (ETA) given by the ship, the port and the terminal must confirm that this time is acceptable and that the facilities are available or, alternatively, advise that the ship must wait at a designated anchorage. The pilot must have received and returned, with comments if appropriate, the passage plan proposed by the ship's master for the transit from port entrance to berth. If the port authority intends to proceed with an inspection of the ship before allowing entry, the master must be advised to proceed to a safe anchorage while the inspection is carried out.

9.2.3 SHIP'S ARRIVAL AND TRANSIT TO THE BERTH

A pilot must be waiting for the ship at the designated meeting point. If, for any reason, the ship cannot proceed, this should have been notified well in advance and not at the last minute, when turning around in the restricted port entrance waters might be difficult and risky. The pilot boarding point must be well out of the port entrance, to allow enough time for a discussion with the master and still be able to abort the ship's entry if necessary. Once on board, and before proceeding within congested waters, the pilot must check with the master if all the propulsion and steering equipment is in working order, if the master agrees with the proposed passage plan and if there are any particular circumstance of which he should be aware. The pilot must advise the master of the position at which the tugs will join the ship, their number and capacity, the availability of an escort boat, and of all navigation aids and rules available or in force in the port. This can include restricted traffic lanes, restricted traffic time, speed limit, Vessel Traffic System (VTS), compulsory number of tugs, compulsory escort boat. The tugs supplied by the port must be able to handle the largest ship expected at the terminal in the worst weather to be expected in the port. They should meet the ship well in advance of the area where they are needed and they should remain available at short notice throughout the duration of the ship's visit, in case an emergency makes it necessary for the ship to depart suddenly. Transit channels from the port entrance to the berth and

①Disaster Prevention Panel
②Premises Monitoring TV
③70 inch Large Screen
④Operator Console
⑤Electricity Panel

77. Control Room in a Large LNG Terminal. (Kansai Electric.)

the turning area in front of the berth must be sized for the largest ship expected at the terminal. When the ship is berthed at the terminal, there should not be any ship traffic passing in the vicinity of the berth.

9.2.4 SHIP ALONGSIDE THE BERTH

The berth, including fenders, mooring hooks and gangway, must be designed to accommodate all types and sizes of ship expected to visit the terminal. The ship's mooring plan should have been reviewed by the terminal and calculations made to confirm that the ship can stay safely alongside with the worst wind speed, wave height and tidal current expected. Once the ship is safely moored alongside, the person in charge of cargo operations at the terminal must visit the ship for a pre-operation meeting. The International Ship/ Shore Safety Check List for Gas Carriers must be completed by the ship and terminal personnel and signed by the persons responsible on each side. The ship Ballast Water Management must be reviewed and samples of ballast water taken if required. Procedures to be followed during the cargo operations, (including: common language, identification of the responsible persons on both sides, communications between ship and terminal, operating limits for stoppage of cargo transfer, disconnection and ship's departure from the berth in relation to weather criteria and procedures to be followed in case of emergency) must be discussed and agreed by ship and terminal personnel. Details of preparations necessary before starting the transfer, (measurement of cargo quantity prior to the transfer, collection of cargo samples, if required, arrangement of the Emergency Shut Down Systems (ESDS) I and II, if appropriate, pressures, temperatures and flow of the product during transfer, warning to be given before stopping the transfer, piping disconnection at the end of transfer, ballasting or deballasting and maintenance of mooring line tensions throughout the transfer) must also be reviewed and agreed by ship and terminal personnel.

When all this is complete, the terminal personnel can proceed with the connection of the ship and shore piping, after careful purging to avoid any liquid spillage. The quantity of cargo on board before transfer is measured and calculated, with the assistance of a shore surveyor, if so required by the charterer. The ESD link is connected and tested. Tank and piping cool-down is started, if required, and the actual transfer can start.

Throughout the transfer, ship and shore personnel will make frequent checks to ensure that there is no cargo leakage, the mooring lines are correctly maintained, that pressures, temperatures and levels in ship and shore tanks are correct, the ballasting or deballasting operation is proceeding and the ship's trim, heel, and hull stresses are maintained within the required limits and that the transfer is, in general, proceeding smoothly.

Once the transfer is complete, the quantity of cargo in the ship's tanks is measured and calculated, the ship and shore piping disconnected after careful purging and the ship is ready to depart. Pilots and tugs will again assist the ship in leaving the berth and navigating through the port exit channels to the open sea.

9.2.5   SAFETY AND CONTINGENCY

Close co-operation between ship and shore personnel is essential for the safe handling of a ship transferring cargo in a terminal. If the operation is well prepared and if open channels of communication are maintained between ship and terminal, there is a good chance that the transfer will be carried out smoothly and that any unexpected incident will be tackled promptly before it can develop into something more serious.

However, due to the hazardous nature of the products handled, an accident is always possible. Ship and terminal personnel must be aware of their respective actions in case of emergency.

A recent joint action by the International Maritime Organization (IMO) and the Environment Office of the United Nations Environment Programme (UNEP IE) has helped to develop the "Awareness and Preparedness for Emergencies at Local Level for Port Areas" (APELL for Port Areas). [6] This programme provides comprehensive technical information on contingency planning for maritime emergencies, including the recently updated and expanded documentation related to oil pollution, prepared in consultation with oil industry organisations and other institutions. Many of its conventions, agreements, regulations, manuals and other guidance documents have great relevance to shipping operations in port areas, including the preparation of contingency planning for emergencies.

In Europe, the "Seveso II Directive", also known as the "Control of Major Accidents Hazards Regulations (COMAH)" [7] is applicable to all sites where a certain quantity of dangerous substances are located. It requires on and off-site emergency plans to be available.

APELL for Port Areas recommends that emergency responses manuals be developed by the terminals, setting down the procedures necessary to give effect to the emergency plan. Their primary function is to provide standing instructions and advice to all involved personnel on the actions they should take in the event of an emergency. Copy of a simplified version of the manual should be given to the ship on arrival. Similarly, the ship should have available, in a safe place near the gangway, or in an office ashore, a copy of their own emergency safety plan.

It is fundamental to safe operation and effective contingency planning that all personnel be thoroughly trained in the procedures they are to follow should there be an incident at the terminal. To this effect, it is recommended that common emergency exercises be conducted at regular intervals. These exercises should not be limited to the ship and terminal personnel but should also involve the ship's operating management, as well as the port authority and the local fire brigade. The involvement of outside shore authorities, of outside shore services such as the fire brigade, and the structure of the chain of command in case of emergency should be clearly defined and the information distributed to all parties. The shore assistance available to the ship in case of fire on board or in the terminal should be specified. In such a case, a decision which is always difficult to make is: Should the ship be kept alongside or

78. LNG Receiving Terminal. (Kansai Electric.)

sent out to sea. The ship should be made aware of terminal policy in this regard.

Attention must also be paid to media relations and the means used to inform the public of events. In particular, in the event of an accident, it is necessary to reassure and advise the local population. It is strongly recommended that the contingency plan identifies those persons authorised to issue public statements; these people must be fully trained in public relations and media handling.

Finally, the preparation, development and implementation of emergency plans should be considered an ongoing process, requiring frequent and regular review [14].

Chapter 10
SHIP-TO-SHIP TRANSFER

10.1 LPG AND PETROCHEMICAL GASES

Ship-to-ship transfer is a very common operation in the oil industry. Over the years, a number of Very Large Crude Carriers (VLCC) or Ultra Large Crude Carriers (ULCC) have systematically discharged all or part of their cargo into smaller ships which, in turn, discharged at ports too small to accommodate the larger ships.

This has also been a common practice in the LPG trade and, to a lesser extent, in the petrochemical gases trade. The procedure has been used at ports too small to accommodate the large ships, or when there was not enough storage available and the larger ship was used as additional storage.

In recent years, many large LPG ships have been anchored off the coasts of India and China, being used as storage vessels. Their cargo was discharged into a fleet of coastal vessels able to reach the shallow domestic ports to discharge in the small storages available or even directly into rail or road trucks or bottling plants. The large vessels were either anchored for long periods, receiving cargo from other ships or they sailed to a loading port, from time to time, to replenish their tanks. This had the added advantage of providing employment for a number of large older ships which, without this opportunity, might have found themselves surplus to requirements. The construction of new terminals, both in India and in China, will reduce greatly the demand for such ships.

The same practice has been used in South America and occasionally in Europe, for instance when a terminal was being serviced.

A recent trend has been the appearance of floating storage units attached to production platforms for oil and LPG. These units are either ships modified for this task or purpose-built units. They receive the warm gas directly from the production platform and cool it, for storage in their tanks. Ships come alongside to collect the gas for transport to the port of delivery. Several such units are already in service and it is probable that more will follow.

A very comprehensive guide book "Ship-to-Ship Transfer Guide (Liquefied Gases)" is compiled by ICS, OCIMF and SIGTTO. [15] This guide gives all necessary recommendations to proceed with a safe ship-to-ship transfer operation.

Without going into too many details, one of the main factors for the success of such an operation is the selection of a safe area, well protected from the weather, with enough space for the two ships to come side by side with plenty of room to manoeuvre. It is also important to choose a period of good weather with low wind speed, reduced wave height and minimum tidal current. The local weather forecasts must be followed with great care. Other factors to consider are the number and quality of fenders available, which should be suitable for the size of ships involved, and the quality of the transfer hoses. The rest of the recommendations are not very different from those listed for a transfer operation in a

79. Two LPG Tankers Side by Side. (SIGTTO.)

terminal: good preparation, detailed exchange of information, careful supervision during the operation and suitable contingency plans in case of emergency.

The critical element, particularly when the transfer involves refrigerated propane or ammonia, is the cargo hoses linking the two ships. Hoses can handle the product at ambient temperature, even at very high pressure, without difficulty. However, the cryogenic element introduced by the low temperature of the transferred product creates a different situation. When combined with the relative movements of the two floating ships, it makes the hoses much more fragile and careful selection and good maintenance are essential if long service is to be expected. The reliability of cargo hoses used for transferring the refrigerated products is very important as, even at the temperature of propane or ammonia, (approximately –45°C or –33°C), a large amount of cold cargo coming into contact with a ship's structure, as the result of a burst hose, can have serious damaging effects on the integrity of the structure. The majority of ship-to-ship transfers has, so far, involved pressurised cargoes. It is only recently, and particularly with the appearance of the production storage units, that the transfer of refrigerated cargo is becoming more common and the suppliers of hoses have had to work on improving their products.

Although an extra element of risk is added in a ship-to-ship transfer operation by the fact that the two ships are not within the protected environment of a safe port, the operation must be reasonably safe as, to my knowledge, there is no record of a serious accident happening in these conditions.

10.2 LNG

Commercial or routine ship-to-ship transfer between LNG ships has never been tried. On several occasions, emergency ship-to-ship transfer of an LNG cargo has been carried out, following an accident or a mechanical problem incapacitating one ship. According to available records, this has been done only four times since the start of LNG shipping, the last time being 15 years ago. In each case, the necessary equipment had to be provided from far away and ample time for extensive preparation was available. An area of very protected waters and the availability of plenty of expertise on site was arranged in time to carry out the operation in the most favourable conditions. All four operations were successfully completed.

Since then, all LNG ship operators have arranged, either individually or within a pool, to have all the necessary material available for such an operation. This includes mainly cargo hoses, fenders, a prefabricated bridge for linking the two ships, and emergency cabling to supply the damaged ship with power, if need be.

There has not, until now, been any need for commercial LNG ship-to-ship transfers to be considered because all LNG projects were fully integrated, with all elements of the chain being available at the same time. The ports were tailored for the ships involved in the project and the storage facilities designed according to requirements.

In recent years, however, some projects have been suggested, which would have involved ship-to-ship transfer, but they did not materialise. Some

serious new proposals are under consideration to provide floating liquefaction and storage units on site for the development of small isolated wells or floating storage and vaporisation units to supply LNG to places where the construction of a storage and vaporisation plant would be either difficult, not considered economical or simply delayed. None of these proposals have yet materialised either. But very serious studies have been conducted and it is probable that, eventually, such a project will be successfully implemented.

Ship-to-ship transfer between LNG ships is not as straight forward as for LPG ships. LNG ships are much larger, although this should not be a serious problem as large oil tankers have been able to find suitable locations. The most serious problem is the potential risk of the accidental release of a large amount of LNG in case of cargo hose damage. In view of the very low temperature of LNG, this would have a devastating effect on the ships' structure. Some known accidental cargo spillages, which occurred during normal cargo transfer in port, even though never very large, have resulted in some frightening damage to the ships involved: extensively cracked decks, even cracked hulls. In the present state of cargo hose technology, and despite the hose suppliers' claim, there is no available hose able to sustain long-term service when handling LNG. Some hoses are adequate for one emergency transfer but their long-term reliability is very doubtful. The other problem of cargo hoses is that, due to the very low temperature of LNG, the hoses are very quickly covered with a thick coat of ice. This makes them loose their flexibility and become much less able to accommodate the relative movements of the two floating ships.

In presenting the report of a Working Group on LNG ship-to-ship transfer, SIGTTO recommends that, until there is a serious improvement in the cryogenic hose technology, only rigid arms must be considered for commercial operations.

In preparation for some floating liquefaction and storage units to be installed on the open sea, where the relative movements of the unit and of the ship would preclude any side by side transfer, much work has been done by a group of oil producers and loading arm suppliers on the possibility of having ships connected in a tandem configuration. The cargo would be transferred through a very long cantilevered arm terminated by an articulated pantograph. The receiving ship would maintain its position behind the floating storage unit through dynamic positioning and would receive the pantograph which would automatically connect to its receiving pipe. This system is claimed to be able to accommodate relative vertical and lateral displacements of several metres. It is, however, still under development.

Commercial LNG ship-to-ship transfer, if envisaged for a specific project, would require extensive planning and preparation. Substantial modifications of the ships to be used would have to be designed and put in place. Extensive surveys of the selected area, statistical research into the prevalent weather and sea conditions and accurate modelling of the relative ship movements would all be necessary. If the operation was planned in the vicinity of an existing port, navigation assistance, in the form of pilotage and tugs, would have to be considered. Finally the authorisation of the local authorities would have to be obtained.

Chapter 11
SAFETY LIQUEFIED GAS OF
MARINE TRANSPORTATION

11.1 SAFETY RECORD

The safety record of the marine transportation of liquefied gases is second to none. Records of shipping accidents have been available, with a good degree of accuracy, since the beginning of the 1980's and there is no record of any gas ship above 5,000 m³ being lost in service since this date. The number of accidents per year has remained roughly the same, even though the number of ships is constantly increasing. The total number of liquefied gas carriers was 722 in 1983, 757 in 1990 and 1009 in 1997 and the total number of accidents for those three years were respectively 48, 45 and 27.

The average age of the liquefied gas fleet is quite high and there is a temptation to suggest that old ships are more accident-prone than newer ships. Obviously much depends on the quality

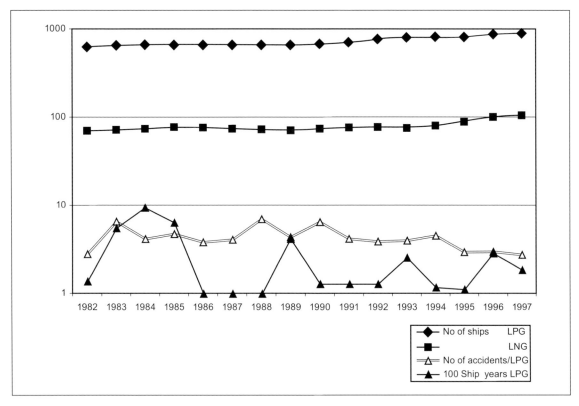

Chart 11.1 Casualty Statistics – LPG and LNG Carriers. (SIGTTO.)

of maintenance applied to the ship throughout its life. A recent survey by a leading classification society has shown that a liquefied gas carrier is most at risk when it is four years old. For the rest of its life, even up to thirty years or more, the number of accidents remains approximately the same. This shows that liquefied gas tankers are, in general, very well maintained and also that they are operated by well-trained crews.

The majority of recorded liquefied gas carrier accidents are caused by reasons not specific to gas carriers, such as navigation, mechanical fault or human error. The number of accidents directly attributable to the cargo containment, machinery and handling is very limited.

The situation regarding terminals is slightly different. There are few reliable statistics of accidents at terminals. It is difficult to get information, except for incidents large enough to be reported in the international press. It is also difficult to differentiate between incidents happening in the storage plant and on the jetty and those happening in the processing plant. There are records of some very large fires occurring in storage plants and refineries, but only a very few actually involved loading jetties and ships.

11.2 HAZARDS AND RISKS

11.2.1 INTRODUCTION

Liquefied gases are classed as hazardous commodities and, since the beginning of their transportation by ship, they have always generated a lot of controversy, particularly Liquid Natural Gas (LNG), of which large quantities are transported on the largest ships of the fleet. Let us try to review the reliability and safety of the marine transportation of liquefied gases, based on the experience of almost 60 years commercial operation.

The previous chapters of this book have described the history and the design, construction and operation of gas carriers and gas terminals and have given a brief overview of those aspects of current practice which aim to avoid accidents and minimise the consequences when accidents do occur. Much of this practice is directed towards the variety of contingencies associated with day-to-day operations. However, in the liquefied gas industry, particular attention is focused on the reduction of the risk of an uncontrolled release of large quantities of combustible liquid or vapour, since such a release could have serious consequences. In a release situation, asphyxiation and frost burns may lead to injuries and fatalities among people at the release site. An ignition of the released gas would result in fire or explosion, considered to be the most serious incidents. Present technology, associated with the existing design, construction and operating standards imposed by the nature of liquefied gases, render the risk of spillage intrinsically low. However, making the most appropriate selection from the various design and contingency options available may not be easy. An up-to-date knowledge of the hazards of liquid and vapour release is necessary. Skilled judgement must be applied to the likelihood of such hazards occurring, in the context of the choices available.

The words **"hazard"** and **"risk"** are frequently used and it is essential to have a clear definition of these terms in the current context. The following definitions are based upon those currently used in hazard and risk assessment reports.

A **Hazard** is a physical situation which has the potential to cause harm. The assessment of a hazard includes the identification of both the undesirable situation and its potential consequences. For example, a storage tank containing liquefied gas is a hazard to the extent that, if it fails, it may release some or all of its contents which will form a vapour cloud. A cloud of flammable vapour is a hazard to the extent that, if it ignites, it may cause damage by radiation or by the generation of over-pressures.

Risk is the probability that a hazard may be realised in a given span of time, or the probability that a person or group of persons, as a result of the hazard occurring, may suffer a specified level of injury in a given timespan. For example, in the case of storage tank failure, the risk may be expressed simply as the probability of failure of the tank in its lifetime or, alternatively, as the probability of injury to a plant operator, or to a given number of people, per year, as a result of tank failure.

From these definitions, it can be deduced that, when a particular hazard is assessed to have the potential for very serious damage, the expected frequency attached to that hazard must be very low, preferably as close to zero as reasonably practicable.

80. LNG Tanker of the Spherical Tank Type.
(The Author.)

Over the years, since the beginning of international trading in liquefied gases, extensive world-wide research has been conducted into potential causes and consequences of spillage. The following paragraphs will give a review of the current knowledge regarding hazard identification and consequences and of the quantification and assessment of risks.

11.2.2 HAZARD IDENTIFICATION

The potential consequences of a major accident are well understood by the liquefied gas industry. A number of systematic techniques to identify hazards have been developed to help prevent accidents.

Identifying hazards is the first and perhaps the most important step in risk management. Without identifying all the hazards, it is impossible to complete the process. Knowing what can go wrong is also a key element in meeting all regulatory requirements. The following methods are those most widely used for the identification of hazards:

- Experience from previous assessments
- Checklists
- Hazard and Operability Studies (HAZOP)
- Failure Mode and Effect Analysis (FMEA)
- WHAT-IF studies
- Task analysis

The latter is a systematic method for analysing a task in terms of its aims and the actions and plans required to achieve those goals. It is a very useful technique to identify hazardous situations created by human error.

Human error is considered to play a part in most industrial accidents. Much has been written on the subject and human factors must definitely be incorporated into the hazard identification techniques.

81. LPG Tanker.

A comprehensive review of hazard identification techniques, as they apply directly to gas tankers and terminals, has been compiled by SIGTTO [10]. Potentially hazardous events, typical prevention measures and further guidance is given on all operational aspects, including:

- Supply of liquefied gas to terminal
- Terminal export to land-based consumers
- Terminal storage
- Terminal refrigeration systems
- Loading system from terminal to ship
- Shore to ship connections from terminal to ship

- Ship reception systems for loading
- Ship off-loading to terminal
- Ship to shore connections for off-loading
- Terminal reception systems for off-loading
- Ship storage tanks and re-liquefaction systems
- Ship berthing
- Ship leaving berth
- Ship movement from sea to berth
- Ship movement from berth to sea
- Ship awaiting loading/off-loading offshore

11.2.3 CONSEQUENCES OF CERTAIN TYPES OF ACCIDENT

We have established above that the main hazard identified in the marine transportation of liquefied gas is without doubt a large release or spillage of refrigerated gas and the subsequent vapour dispersion and/or combustion. Extensive studies have been conducted to understand these processes and there is abundant literature available. This chapter will briefly review the technology available to reach a better understanding of these subjects.

LNG and refrigerated LPG, as discussed here, are described as boiling liquids. They are stored at temperatures a few degrees above their boiling point, where their vapour pressure is slightly above that of ambient air pressure. If a release takes place to the atmosphere, any of the following could occur simultaneously:

- Outflow of liquid into the surrounding environment
- Liquid spreading on the substrate to form a pool

- Evaporation or boiling to give a vapour which is heavier than air above the pool due to its temperature and/or its molecular weight

- Dispersion of the gas by the wind and its subsequent dilution with air.

The first aspect to consider in the prediction of the consequences of any accidental release is the rate at which LNG or LPG would be released into the environment and what quantity would be released. Both answers will depend on parameters such as the size and shape of the tank, the position of the orifice, the nature of the product, pressures and temperatures inside and outside the tank and whether the leak occurs on land or in water. The literature describes the physics resulting in semi-empirical models for the spreading and evaporation of LPG and LNG on land and water. [18]

The next calculation would be to determine the behaviour of the vapour cloud originating from the pool of liquid. In all cases the vapour boiling or evaporating from a pool of liquid LPG or LNG is, at first, heavier than air. Many alternative models have been developed to describe the physical processes taking place in heavy vapour dispersion. At a distance from the source, the heavy vapour may become neutrally buoyant, due to dilution with air and the modelling process can be continued, using more conventional passive dispersion models. Many examples have been documented of these simple "integral" types of heavy gas dispersion and passive dispersion models. The use of these models always includes a number of uncertainties and attempts have been made to obtain more accurate results by using "3D" models or by physical modelling in wind tunnels.

82. Fire in a LPG Storage Facility. (SIGTTO.)

The vapour of liquefied gases is invisible, but often a white cloud, produced by condensation from the surrounding air, can be seen after a release of refrigerated liquid. The correlation between the boundary of the visible cloud and the boundary of gas flammability varies with the product spilled and the humidity of the air. For LNG released onto water, the limit of the cloud will correspond to the limit of flammability of the released gas. However, this is not always so and, in some cases, in particular LPG, the limit of flammability can extend far beyond the boundaries of the visible cloud.

At some stage, the gas cloud dispersing downwind will have diluted to a non-flammable concentration, at which point it cannot be ignited. At the flammable concentration boundary, typically close to the Lower Flammable Limit (LFL) of the vapour air mixture, the gas cloud can ignite and, if unobstructed, burn back to the source pool as a "flash-fire". The extent of the flash-fire can be predicted, using the dispersion models previously described and taking the approximate LFL concentration as the concentration of interest. The flash-fire will probably burn back to the liquid surface of the pool, resulting in a pool fire. The thermal radiation from pools of flammable liquid burning on the ground is typically estimated on the basis of semi-empirical models which have been developed from field experiments.

The fire and explosion models to be used contain various simplifying assumptions and rely on empirical parameters to determine the physical loadings (thermal and blast) at a particular point. These features all introduce an element of uncertainty into the results of a particular fire or explosion consequence assessment.

The greatest difficulties in predicting the effects of fire lie in:

- Defining the precise shape and orientation of the flame with respect to the target.

- Defining the flame emissive power.

In certain circumstances, LNG in contact with water at ambient temperature can give rise to very rapid vaporisation, with resultant shock waves both in the air, as vapour is energetically expelled, and in the water. This is known as Rapid Phase Transition (RPT). The explosion is purely physical with no possibility of ignition but with large release of energy. Further research is still being carried out to try to achieve a more complete understanding of this complex phenomenon.

Carbon steel and certain other metals, which are not intended for use at low temperatures, can become brittle and fracture under stress due to their reduced strength when the temperature falls below a certain point. Cryogenic embrittlement of a vessel or pipe-work containing flammable liquid can lead to failure and the direct escape of liquid or vapour to atmosphere. Suitable materials must be selected for the range of temperatures encountered in normal operations. This must be confirmed by a rigorous quality control and assurance system. The selected materials should also be suitable for low temperatures which might occur under abnormal conditions such as:

- Abnormally low ambient temperatures.

- Emergency depressurisation of liquefied gases stored under pressure.

- Localised cooling on expansion at the point of leakage at valves, flanges and fittings.

- Transfer, by accident or mishandling, of low temperature fluids into a plant intended for higher temperatures.

- The sub-cooling of the LNG or LPG.

11.2.4 FREQUENCY OF ACCIDENT SCENARIOS

a) *General* – The risks from marine transportation, storage and handling of flammable liquefied gases may be estimated from an evaluation of the frequency and consequences of hazards arising from these operations. These hazards can be estimated using three different approaches:

- From the statistical records of operational events.

- Using historical data for similar equipment used in related or similar applications.

- Through detailed analysis of the relevant system and by studying the potential causes of the incidents.

Incidents may be divided into two categories:

- Those occurring at the terminal, including the jetty, expressed in terms of likelihood per visit.

- Those arising in transit or during port approaches, expressed in terms of frequency per loaded mile.

b) *Frequency of Ship Incidents* – There are five main concerns with regard to ship operations:

- Collision – where two vessels under way run into each other.

- Striking – where a vessel moored in a port, alongside a berth, or a jetty is struck by a passing vessel.

- Impact – where a vessel runs into a dock wall or jetty.

- Grounding – where a vessel runs onto shore or submerged rocks.

- Fire/explosion – where a fire on the vessel spreads to involve the cargo, or where an explosion is initiated in the cargo itself.

In addition to these main concerns, the following potential concerns are also considered in each case, but are usually found to be negligible when compared with other risks:

- Foundering/capsize – where the ship sinks in rough weather or because of leaks.

- Structural failure – where the cargo tank cracks due to fatigue, wave load, vibration or adverse cargo load distribution.

- Aircraft strike – where an aeroplane or helicopter crashes into the ship.

- Spontaneous failure – where a manufacturing defect leads to an apparently spontaneous failure of the cargo tank.

- Refrigeration failure – where breakdown of the refrigeration plant on a liquefied gas ship leads to the cargo boiling and escaping.

- Domino accident – where an accident on one ship either causes or is caused by an accident on a nearby ship.

Data may be available for existing facilities from the Port Authority or from the operator's own incident records. Where generic data is not appropriate for a particular situation, simulation methods may be adopted, to estimate ship incidents and release frequencies.

When assessing the critical speeds at which collisions and groundings would cause significant damage to a vessel, account should be taken of the following factors:

- The angle of approach and the location of impact on the struck ship.

- Whether the struck ship was moored alongside or floating free.

- The effect of added water mass on the dissipation of energy in the water.

- The draft and freeboard of the striking ship in relation to those of the struck ship.

83. LNG Tanker Alongside Berth. (The Author.)

- The apportionment of energy absorbed between the two ships, taking into account the form and stiffness of the striking ship's bow.

- The degree of distortion which may be suffered by the cargo containment prior to its rupture.

- The significance of dynamic loading of structures during the collision process.

Predictive speed should be applied with due consideration to the assumptions made and the various associated uncertainties.

The probability of cargo loss in a specific incident would be obtained by estimating the proportion of incidents which would breach the integrity of the cargo tanks.

c) *Frequency of Terminal Incidents* – Operations at a liquefied gas terminal that are of interest in a risk assessment consist primarily of cargo transfers. Incidents may be considered within the following categories:

- Cargo transfer failure – where cargo is spilled while the vessel is loading or unloading. This includes the overfilling of tanks during loading.

- Ranging and mooring failure – where cargo is spilled due to manifold connection failure resulting from excessive movement of the ship alongside during loading or unloading.

- Domino accident – where an accident on one ship either causes or is caused by an accident in a storage or process plant or on another ship.

Incidents at liquefied gas terminals are recorded on a few data bases. Other sources of data may be available for the site under consideration from the Port Authority or the operator's own incident record.

Modelling techniques, such as fault and event trees, part-count procedures, etc., may be applied to represent a particular facility. In assessing the frequency of spills at a particular facility, the effects of the following features may be taken into account:

- Quick-release couplings on the connections.

- Level and other alarms and trips.

Accident scenarios may be developed, taking into account these and other features, to determine the frequency of particular consequences.

d) *Other Hazards* – The likelihood of hazards other than those involving ship and terminal operations can be estimated in the same way as described above. For example, these could involve earthquakes, severe weather hazards, events involving aircraft and other impacts, escalated events due to other industrial sites located near-by.

e) *Ignition of Releases* – A release of flammable liquefied gas will present the greatest hazard when ignited. The frequency of the release combined

84. LNG Tanker with Loading Arms Connected.

with the probability of the release ignition will give the risk to be expected from the incident. The following events can be potential causes of a release ignition:

- Ignition by the release event

- Static electricity

- External ignition sources

The estimated probability of ignition of vapour clouds is often based upon judgement, taking into consideration general statistics of ignition from accidental releases. These statistics tend to show that small leaks are unlikely to ignite but that the probability of ignition increases with the size of the release.

11.2.5 RISK ASSESSMENT

In previous pages, the major hazards to be considered in the assessment of the risks which may arise from the operation of a liquefied gas facility have been reviewed. This would represent

the first part of a risk analysis procedure. Such a procedure is generally used to confirm the design of new liquefied gas facilities or to review the

85. Ship in Dry Dock. (The Author.)

safety and cost-efficiency of existing operating facilities. The review of possible safety measures and of their cost effectiveness would complete the procedure.

When designing a new facility, a preliminary safety assessment can be made, for example, at the start of planning, to help decide between several options based on their cost-effectiveness.

It is recommended to undertake regular safety audits or safety reviews of operating liquefied gas facilities to ensure continuing high standards of management, operation and maintenance. Risk assessment can be used following such audits, to evaluate the need for extra alarm and control systems or extra safety equipment.

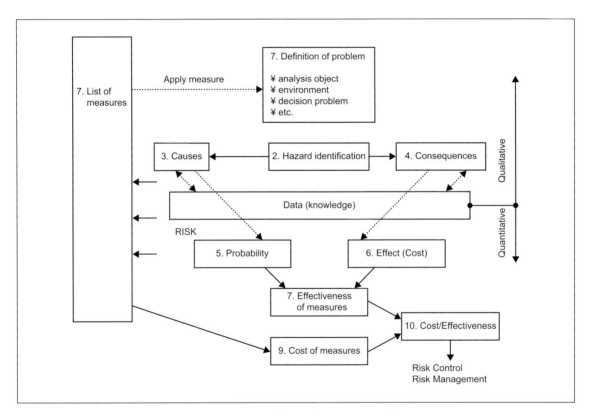

Figure 11.1 Risk Analysis Framework.

Chapter 12
SOME STORIES!...

This chapter describes some of the most serious but also very typical accidents which have unfortunately marred the marine transportation of liquefied gases through the years.

A small number of representative accidents have been selected, not for their headline making aspect, but because they illustrate so well that accidents, even the very serious ones, almost invariably, start from very banal causes. It is the accumulation of small faults or small blunders which makes the small mishap develop into the final disaster. There are lessons to be learned from all incidents or accidents; this is why the reporting of all incidents, accidents and near misses is so important, not only for the marine transportation of liquefied gases but for all other industries as well.

I have allowed myself to include a few incidents in which I, or more accurately the ships I was responsible for, were involved. Just to show that operating ships, particularly when they are gas tankers, can sometimes be a lot of fun!

12.1 ACCIDENTS INVOLVING LNG AND LPG STORAGE TANKS

12.1.1 THE CLEVELAND, OHIO LNG TANK FAILURE – OCTOBER 1944

This is, without doubt, the worst accident involving an LNG shore tank and it is the only recorded accident in the history of the LNG industry to cause substantial loss of life.

The Cleveland site, in Ohio, U.S.A., was the first LNG peak-shaving plant built in the world. The storage facility included three spherical tanks of 2,350 m³ capacity each, built in 1940 and one toro-segmental tank of 4,250 m³ capacity, built in 1943. This tank was of unusual design, being supported by pillars. Although the manufacturers claimed that they had more confidence in determining stresses in a toro-segmental tank than in a spherical tank, problems had been experienced with that tank during commissioning, when a crack developed the first time it was cooled down. Following this, a small bund was constructed around the tanks, designed to contain any small leaks from possible further cracks.

The four tanks were constructed of 3.5% nickel steel for the inner tank and carbon steel for the outer tank. The insulation was cork and rockwool. The mechanical properties of 3.5% nickel steel were known to be unacceptable for the LNG temperature of –160°C, with a great facility to initiate cracking, which could lead to catastrophic failure. However, other more suitable materials were disregarded and 3.5% nickel steel was used for reasons of wartime shortages and cost saving.

The toro-segmental tank failed catastrophically within a short period of being filled to capacity for the first time. The damage was caused by ground vibration from either a locomotive or a steam hammer, initiating cracking in the brittle tank.

The contents of the tank over-flowed the inadequate bund and entered the common drainage system. Vapour was ignited, most probably from sources of ignition in neighbouring factories and LNG that came in contact with water in the drains caused rapid phase transition explosions, cratering the site. The resulting fire caused the support legs on one of the spherical tanks to buckle and collapse, adding a further 1000 tons of LNG to the disaster. The remaining two tanks survived the incident intact and without loss of contents.

The main cause of the accident was the wrong choice of materials. The following factors aggravated the disaster:

- Poor site layout and design

- Undersized bund walls

- Close pitching of the tanks (3 metres)

- Poorly designed drainage system

- The proximity of local housing and factories provided sources of ignition and certainly contributed to the high death toll.

This accident resulted in 128 people being killed and between 200 and 400 others injured and stopped the development of peak-shaving facilities in the United States for many years.

12.1.2 FEYZIN REFINERY AND STORAGE FACILITIES – FRANCE – 1966

The bursting of several large LPG pressure vessels at the Feyzin refinery in France, in 1966, was one of the worst accidents involving Liquefied Petroleum Gas (LPG). The standards for storing and handling LPG were revised in many countries following this incident.

A 1,200 m^3 pressurised spherical storage vessel, almost full of propane, was to be drained to eliminate some water. The drain pipe was equipped with two 2" valves in series. The two valves were opened to proceed with draining. When traces of oil showed that the operation was nearly complete, the valve nearest to the tank was shut and then cracked to complete the procedure. As no flow was coming, the valve was opened fully again. It is presumed that the valve was blocked by a plug of hydrates which was suddenly released, splashing the three operators present with liquid propane. The valve nearest to the tank lost its handle which the operators could not get back on. The second valve froze and could not be moved. The drain valves were located immediately below the tank, which was only 1.4 m above ground, making their access difficult.

A visible cloud of vapour, 1 metre deep, extended over 150 metres. This cloud was ignited 25 minutes after the leak, by a car on the nearby road. The road had been closed by the police, but the car approached via a side road. The fire flashed back to the sphere, which was surrounded by flames. There was no immediate explosion. The sphere was fitted with a water spray, but the supply was only designed to deliver half of the quantity of water normally recommended (8 litres/m^2 minute) and this was not sufficient. When the fire brigade started to use their hoses, the supply to the spheres ran dry. The firemen seemed to have used most of the available water for cooling neighbouring spheres to stop the fire from spreading, in the belief that the relief valve would protect the burning vessel. To make matters worse, the ground under the sphere was level so that any propane that did not evaporate or burn immediately, collected under the sphere and continued to burn.

Ninety minutes after the fire started, the sphere burst. Ten of the 12 firemen within a radius of 50 metres were killed. Men 140 metres away were badly burned by a wave of propane coming over the compound wall. Flying debris broke the legs of an adjacent sphere which toppled over. Its relief valve discharged liquid which added to the fire and, 45 minutes later, this sphere also burst. In total, seven spheres and two other pressure vessels burst or exploded and three more were damaged. The fire spread to gazoline and fuel oil tanks. A total of 18 persons were killed and at least 80 others injured.

It was originally thought that the spheres exploded because their relief valves were too small. However, the investigation revealed that the metal in the upper portion of the spheres, above the liquid level, was weakened by the heat and lost its strength. Below the liquid level, the boiling liquid kept the metal cool. Incidents such as this, in which a vessel explodes because the metal gets too hot, are known as Boiling Liquid Expanding Vapour Explosions or BLEVEs. When a tank without insulation is subjected to the heat of a fire, if the liquid level is low and cannot protect the top of the tank by absorbing the heat, the tank walls may overheat and burst at or below the set pressure of the relief valve. The relief valve will not prevent the vessel bursting.

To prevent the occurrence of such incidents, many companies modified the design of tank draining facilities, including, in particular, the fitting of remote-operated valves and combustible gas detectors to provide early warning of a leak. Other modifications were also introduced to prevent a fire from escalating.

Much research has since been conducted on the occurrence of BLEVEs, one of the most frightening accidents which can occur in a fire in an LPG storage facility.

12.1.3 LPG STORAGE AND DISTRIBUTION CENTRE IN MEXICO CITY – NOVEMBER 1984

In November 1984, a disaster involving an LPG installation occurred in Mexico City and resulted in the deaths of over 500 people. In terms of casualties, this was probably the worst accident involving liquefied petroleum gases [27].

The LPG storage and distribution centre, built in 1962, is situated to the North of Mexico City. The storage consisted of four spheres with a volume of 1,600 m^3 and two spheres of 2,400 m^3, with an additional 48 horizontal cylinders of various dimensions. The pressure relief valves were set at approximately 10.3 bar. The storage location was divided into separate sections by concrete walls, about 1 metre high. The storage centre was supplied by three underground pipelines from refineries and the LPG was distributed in the same way, also via tank cars and gas cylinders. At the time of the disaster, the whole storage centre may have contained 11,000 to 12,000 m^3. It was only after construction of the storage site that housing was introduced in the vicinity. The built-up area started some 130 metres from the storage tanks and consisted of simple one and two-storey houses built in brick or wood.

In the early morning of Monday 19 November 1984, a chain of events at the LPG storage facility in Mexico City led to one of the major disasters in the history of industrial activity.

LPG leakage, followed by ignition, caused a number of explosions, which almost completely destroyed the storage facility. Five people were killed and two were injured at the site. The effect in the built-up area south of the storage area was truly dramatic. Approximately 500 people were killed and over 7,000 seriously injured, the majority while they slept. Later, about 200,000 people were evacuated. Between 5.45 a.m. and 7.01 a.m., nine explosions were registered on the seismograph of Mexico City University located 20 miles away. The second and the seventh explosions were the most severe, with an intensity of 0.5 on the Richter Scale. The second explosion occurred within one minute of the first.

Although no direct cause of the accident has ever been officially established, it seems that a large quantity of LPG leaked from a pipeline or a tank. The LPG dispersed over the walls into the surrounding areas and the vapour cloud had reached a height of 2 metres when it was ignited. A flash fire resulted, followed by explosions in various places. The vapour cloud is assumed to have penetrated houses, which were consequently destroyed by internal explosions. The vapour explosion was probably the first of nine that were registered. It caused a huge sea of flames in the storage area. After one minute, a second violent explosion (BLEVE) occurred. A number of reports stated that one or two cylinders were thrown about over large distances. Two spheres may also have exploded at the same time.

Over-heating and/or penetration by fragments of other tanks were responsible for the BLEVEs.

The very short interval between the vapour cloud explosion and the initial BLEVE, if combined with other reasonably reliable information, tends to confirm the supposition that overfill may have occurred in the case of one or more tanks.

The four smaller spheres were completely destroyed, with fragments scattered across the area. The largest spheres remained intact, although their legs had buckled from the heat, causing them to fall to the ground. Only four of the 48 cylinders were left in their original concrete supports. Twelve cylinders were thrown over 100 metres, one landing some 400 metres away and two over 1,000 metres. One large sphere fragment landed at a distance of about 700 metres. The area in which housing was, for the most part, destroyed was the area where the majority of casualties occurred and extended roughly 300 metres from the centre of the storage site.

86. Mexico Storage Facility after the Accident. (SIGTTO.)

A lot of lessons were learned from this devastating accident, which was probably caused by a combination of design and operating errors. Standards for the lay-out of storage terminals were modified and the use of mounded horizontal cylinders was strongly recommended.

12.2 TWO ACCIDENTS INVOLVING LNG TANKERS

12.2.1 THE EL PASO PAUL KAISER – JULY 1979

On the morning of 29 June 1979, a 125,000 m³ LNG tanker left Arzew, Algeria bound for the East Coast of the United States, with a cargo of 95,000 m³ of LNG. Due to a small defect, Tank No 5 was left empty which explained why the ship was not carrying a full cargo of 125,000 m³ [28].

The cargo containment system was a five tank Gaz Transport Membrane type and the ship was starting her 13th voyage.

On the same evening, shortly before midnight, with reasonable visibility and following a series of unfortunate manoeuvres, the ship became stranded, at a speed of approximately 17 knots, on La Perla Pinnacle, on the north side of the Straits of Gibraltar.

The stranded ship had a forward draft of 16.2 metres, an aft draft of 10.7 metres and a list to starboard of 5.5 degrees. Engineering analysis determined that it would be safe to refloat the ship without transferring the cargo.

An extensive salvage operation was organised and the ship was refloated on the afternoon of 4 July and was assisted by salvage tugs to a safe anchorage on the west side of Gibraltar.

87. El Paso Paul Kayser in Dry Dock. (The Author.)

147

The decision was made to transfer the whole of her LNG cargo onto a sister ship and the necessary permission was granted by the Spanish authorities. This would be the first time that such a ship-to-ship transfer operation would be attempted between two LNG tankers. Fortunately, a grounding manual had been prepared by the owner the year before, including in the contents a list of material necessary to conduct a ship-to-ship transfer operation.

All the listed specialised equipment, in particular the cryogenic hoses and fittings, had to be purchased and transported to the ship. A wooden platform was built, to be installed between the two vessels. Pneumatic fenders, necessary for mooring the ships together, were found to be available locally.

An assessment of the damage was made, to allow naval architects to establish an unloading plan which would minimise the risk of further structural damage or possible breaching of the inner hull and the cargo containment system.

A balance between several factors had to be made, to obtain a safe discharge sequence. The main considerations were:

- Minimising the hull stress and bending moment, primarily in way of the damage

- Maintaining the ship afloat

- Maintaining the loading manifolds of both ships at approximately the same level

- Minimising the use of the damaged ship's ballast system

Extensive use was made of computer damage stability programmes from the ship's company head office and of the loading computer on board. In addition, a finite element structural analysis of the ship's inner bottom was carried out to evaluate its residual strength.

A quite elaborate discharge sequence was designed, combining alternative cargo discharge with water ballast movements, achieved by pressurisation of the water ballast capacities.

88. Primary Membrane in Tank No. 1. (The Author.)

The two ships were successfully moored side by side and the transfer operation started on the morning of 9 July and lasted little more than 41 hours. The weather remained perfect and a total quantity of 93,161 m³ was transferred at an average rate of 2,250 m³/hour, with no loss of cargo during the transfer.

Following the transfer, the ship was warmed up normally, inerted and aerated in preparation for proceeding to a repair yard.

The extensive damage to the starboard side of the hull is shown on photo No. 87. Despite this extensive damage, the cargo tanks remained intact and the only consequences were damage to the secondary membrane at the after part of Tank No. 1 forward part of Tank No. 2 and disformation of the primary membrane on the after part of No. 1 Tank. Fortunately, Tank No. 1 remained liquid tight and there was no leakage of LNG (See photo No. 88). Sketch No. 12.1 shows the extent of membrane which had to be removed for repair in each of the two tanks. This shows the extreme resilience of this type of containment system.

Repairs were completed in January 1980 and the ship was then ready to re-enter service.

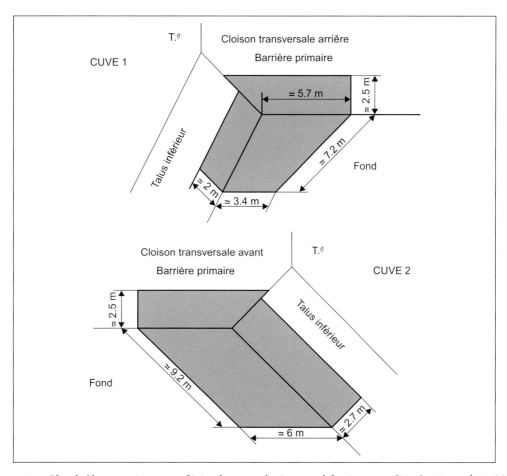

Figure 12.1 Sketch Showing Amount of Membrane to be Removed for Repairs of Tanks No. 1 & 2. (GTT.)

12.2.2 LNG TAURUS – 1979

Late in 1979 LNG "Taurus", a 125,000 m³ LNG tanker with a cargo containment system of the five tank Kvaerner-Moss self-supporting spherical type, was bound for Tobata, Japan with a full cargo of LNG from Indonesia. The LNG Taurus and her sister ships had discharged in this port many times since 1977, when the Indonesia to Japan project started and the crews were very familiar with the port and the usual procedures in force. Arrival at the pilot station was scheduled for early morning as usual and it was common practice, in case of bad weather, for the ship to pick-up the pilot inside the protected waters of the bay.

On that particular day, the weather was slightly rough but no special warning had been received and the Master was anticipating a routine discharge. However, when the vessel entered the bay, expecting to pick up the pilot at the usual location, they were told that the terminal was closed and that the ship should stay outside until further notice. Unfortunately, the ship was already too far inside the bay to be able to turn around without entering. They attempted to turn inside the bay but eventually ended up stranded on solid rocks, at a speed of approximately 12 knots.

The ship's bottom sustained extensive damage but, fortunately, the cargo containment system remained intact and after successful salvage and discharge of the cargo, the ship was dry-docked for repairs. The damage resulting from the grounding was almost completely to the outer shell of bottom plating and the stiffeners between the inner and outer hulls. There was very little deformation of the inner hull and no deformation to any of the tank support structures or the tanks themselves. Slightly more than 2,000 tonnes of steel had to be replaced.

These two last incidents are the only serious accidents involving LNG tankers. In both cases, with two different cargo containment systems, despite very serious damage to the ship's hull, the integrity of the cargo containment was not affected and no casualties were directly attributable to the accident.

12.3 ACCIDENTS INVOLVING LPG TANKERS

12.3.1 THE YUYO MARU COLLISION – NOVEMBER 1974

This was probably the worst accident involving a liquefied gas tanker. On 9th November 1974, the LPG tanker Yoyu Maru, Japanese flag, built in 1966, with approximately 47,200 m³ of LPG tank capacity, was proceeding through the Tokyo Bay to Kawasaki, to discharge a cargo of propane, butane and naphtha loaded in Ras Tanura, Saudi Arabia. The ship was designed to carry refrigerated propane and butane in special LPG tanks and naphtha in the side ballast tanks and the forward deeptank. Although this configuration is not allowed by the IMO IGC code, the code only applies to ships built after 1980. In this instance, the ship was loaded with 35,553 m³ of fully refrigerated propane, 10,796 m³ of fully refrigerated butane and 35,553 m³ of naphtha. The ship was proceeding at about 12 knots, assisted by an escort boat, in accordance with local regulations [26].

The cargo ship "Pacific Aries", Liberian flag, built in 1968, 10,874 gross tons, loaded with 14,835 tons of steel materials, had just left the port of Kisarazu in the Tokyo Bay and was proceeding towards Hokkaido at a speed of about 7 knots. The weather was good, with two miles' visibility.

At about 13.37 hours, the bow of the "Pacific Aries" struck the starboard bow area of the "Yuyo Maru" almost at a right angle. On the "Yuyo Maru", one of the naphtha tanks was damaged, resulting in the escape of a large amount of naphtha which immediately caught fire. The "Pacific Aries" had her bow crushed and was instantly covered with the burning naphtha coming from the "Yuyo Maru". As they were in the middle of the traffic lane, both ships were towed to other areas of the bay. The "Yuyo Maru" was stranded and the "Pacific Aries" was anchored.

On the "Pacific Aries", the fire was reasonably under control at about 17.00 hours the same day. Due to the extreme intensity of the blaze, 27 crew members died almost immediately following the collision. The only survivor was the second engineer who stayed in the control area of the engine room wearing a breathing apparatus during the worst of the fire. He was only discovered the next morning.

On "Yuyo Maru", 5 members of the crew of 38 were killed and 7 were injured. The flames were estimated to be 60 metres high, black smoke billowing to 300 meters. Despite the rapid arrival of fire-fighting facilities, access on board was impossible due to the extreme heat and the fire continued unabated for many days, with some large explosions sending flames higher than 100 metres. Eventually, the fire extended to reach more naphtha tanks on the starboard side. The LPG tanks remained intact until 13th November, when gas started burning on top of the level gauges and the manholes. On 20th November, the fire was still active and the vessel was towed out of the Tokyo Bay. The vessel was 23 nautical miles offshore on the afternoon of the 21st when fire and explosions became so fierce that it was decided to abort the towing operation. The vessel was left to drift and continued burning until 27th November, when it was decided to sink it. Even this was not easy and it took two days of bombing by four ships and four planes, along with torpedo attacks by a submarine to eventually send the ship to the bottom on 28th November in the afternoon, 18 days after the collision.

It is interesting to note that, despite the raging inferno created by the burning naphtha, it took five days for the fire to start affecting the LPG tanks. Prior to that, LPG vapour was only burning at the top of the safety valve masts.

Following the accident, the rules of navigation in the Tokyo Bay were reviewed and, more importantly, the design of LPG tankers allowing the transport of petroleum products in the side tanks was forbidden.

12.3.2 THE GAS FOUNTAIN – IRAQ/ IRAN WAR – OCTOBER 1984

During the 1980's, the Iran/Iraq conflict took a large toll on shipping in the Persian Gulf. Gas tankers were more fortunate and one of the few to be hit was a 40,232 m³, fully refrigerated LPG carrier built in 1969. The ship can be considered as one of the first generation of fully refrigerated LPG ships [29].

This was the first occasion that a liquefied gas carrier was breached with ensuing fire and then successfully salvaged. This incident provides a practical demonstration of the sound design concepts of these vessels.

The ship is a conventional LPG ship, designed with three free-standing prismatic cargo tanks, able to carry fully refrigerated propane and other liquefied gases of similar characteristics. Each tank is surrounded with loose perlite insulation and is contained in a hold surrounded by side and bottom water ballast tanks. Each hold and the engine room are separated by cofferdams.

Each tank is equipped with two submerged electric pumps located at the aft part and one electric deepwell pump located at the centre. The cargo liquefaction plant is installed in a single deck house, amidships. A cargo control room is located within the fore part of the ail-aft accomodation.

The ship had loaded 6,300 tonnes of propane in tank No. 1 and 12,140 tonnes of butane in tanks No. 2 and 3 at Ras Tanura and sailed on 11th October 1984 for Fujairah outside the Gulf.

During the morning of 12th October, when in the middle of the Gulf, the ship was stalked by an Iranian aircraft which subsequently attacked with air-to-ground armour piercing rockets. Three rockets hit the vessel.

The crew, understandably, promptly operated the cargo emergency shut-down system, stopped the ship's engine, closed doors between accommodation and engine room and abandoned ship in the life boats. They were subsequently rescued and returned home without injury.

One rocket exploded on-deck, above the fore end of tank No. 2, near the centre line. The deck was breached in two places but tank No. 2 was undamaged. All piping and electric cables above deck were damaged and some liquid cargo was released and caught fire.

The other two rockets hit the deck on the aft port side of tank No. 3. One apparently exploded above deck, doing little damage. The other penetrated the deck at an oblique angle and travelled some 4 to 5 metres forward in the hold space above the cargo tank before detonating. The explosion lifted a section of the deck and also opened the tank roof over an area of about 3 × 2 metre. This tank was full of butane which, during its initial and continued release, established a large fire on deck above the shell entry hole. It has been estimated that some 220 m^3 of liquid butane was released during the initial depressurisation of the tank. This probably lasted for the first 60 minutes after the initial penetration. During this first phase, the fire was similar in characteristics to a large turbulent torchlike flame, reaching heights of up to 200 metres and creating heat damage on deck. Thereafter the fire stabilised, being fed by gas boil-off escaping through the hole in the tank.

Openings in the accommodation house probably due to shattered windows and the high thermal radiation occurring in the first stages of the fire, led to the ignition of multiple fires which completely gutted it. The fact that doors between the accommodation house and the engine room were found closed, probably prevented the fire spreading through the engine room. However, all electric cables on deck and in the accommodation were completely destroyed.

This was the situation when the salvage tug made contact with the ship on 13th October. After intensive water cooling of the main fire areas, the gas fires were extinguished with powerful water jets, first over tank No. 3 and then the torch fire over tank No. 2.

89. Model of a LPG Tanker Similar to Gas Fountain.

Although this is contrary to the usual advice not to extinguish gas fires, in this instance it was necessary, as there was no possibility of isolating the leaks. Had the ship been left to float around, the fires would have continued burning until the whole cargo was consumed.

The vessel was then taken in tow towards Dubai, to escape from an area of possible further aerial attacks and to prevent gas build-up now that the fires were extinguished. A salvage team was put together and started the comprehensive and complicated task of preparing the vessel for transhipment of the cargo. The following actions were taken:

- Securing the vessels gastight integrity.
- Control of the cargo tank pressures.
- Establishing a controllable trim and list situation.
- Reactivation of the electrical supply and essential services from the engine room.
- Repair of the fire protection and fire-fighting systems.
- Preparation of cargo pumps and cargo piping for transhipment.
- Preparation of a transhipment schedule.

Finally, on 15th November 1984, just one month after the attack, all the remaining cargo was successfully transferred onto another vessel.

The quantity of cargo transferred was 17,204.2 tonnes of propane and butane. The total quantity lost during the incident was therefore about 1,200 tonnes. The quantity lost during the attack and subsequent venting during the next ten days was estimated at 350 tonnes. Thereafter, once the tanks were reinstated in a tight situation, manual venting was continued to control the tank pressure. The quantity vented was estimated as follows:

- Tank No 1 with propane: 12-13 tonnes/day.
- Tank No 2 partly full with butane: 8 tonnes/day.
- Tank No 3 with butane: 7-8 tonnes/day.

It is interesting to note that, even after such a serious attack, the damage to the LPG tanker was such that most of the cargo could be saved and the ship was eventually left in a repairable condition.

12.4 SOME OTHER INCIDENTS FROM MY OWN RECORDS

12.4.1 A BAD NIGHT IN ZVETINA – LIBYA

Sometime during the winter of 1974, a ship, which was part of the fleet for which I had the technical responsibility, was loading LPG in Zvetina, Libya. The ship was a five year old, 9,000 m^3 semi-pressurised LPG tanker. Her schedule was to complete loading in the evening and depart immediately for the discharge port. In the middle of the night, I was awakened by a call from the ship's captain via the radio-telephone, advising that, while leaving Zvetina in good weather and good visibility and with the assistance of a local pilot, the ship had missed the turn at the end of the channel and was grounded by the bow on the rocky bottom at the side of the channel. The rest of the night was occupied with establishing, with the ship's crew, that their situation, although regrettable, was not immediately critical and with setting in motion the Company Emergency Procedures. As the ship's position was not critical and the weather forecast reasonable, it was decided to try to get the ship free at high tide under her own power. Unfortunately this was not successful but, as the tide coefficients were on the increase, it was

90. LPG Tanker Involved in the Incident in Libya. (The Author.)

decided to try again at the next high tide. There was already a tug outside, offering salvage but, as yet, there was no urgency.

A small ship had been chartered to attempt a transhipment of part of the cargo but, it was risky to carry out such an operation in the channel, particularly with the swell which was consistent with a tendency to increase. The ship was labouring on the rocks and it was obvious that something would have to be done soon to avoid further damage.

The possibility of venting part of the cargo was discussed with the shore authorities and authorisation was apparently received from none other that Colonel Gadafi himself. However, this was also difficult in view of the proximity of the refinery which would need to be shut down for the duration of the operation. Time and high tides went by until suddenly, after six days, with one wave stronger than the others and the engine full astern, the ship decided to leave

the rocks and remain afloat, albeit with a very substantial negative trim. This was sufficient to take her to anchor outside and to organise a ship-to-ship transfer onto the little ship which had been waiting all this time. Two thousand tonnes of cargo were transferred and a second ship was waiting to take the rest. Unfortunately, the weather was worsening and a second ship-to-ship transfer operation became too dangerous. Stress calculations having confirmed that the ship could safely sail, authorisation was obtained from the classification society for the two ships to make their way together to Pireus, Greece, where the rest of the cargo was transferred and the damaged ship repaired.

This created an unexpected windfall for the Pireus customs officers and for the local cement transport company. The cargo tank insulation was bulk perlite and the perlite had to be removed from the forward hold to repair the ship's bottom. As the perlite was wet, it had been transformed into a whitish muddy substance which needed to be pumped out and disposed of. The local authorities allowed its transport to the City refuse dump and the cement transport trucks were ideally equipped for this. However, the customs officers were highly suspicious of this white powdery substance, even in its very muddy condition and they insisted that each truck be accompanied to the refuse dump by a customs officer. Thus, a worrying episode ended on a lighter note.

12.4.2 A FEW QUIET DAYS OFF THE MEXICAN WEST COAST

In 1975, a new addition was made to the fleet for which I had the technical responsibility. This was a 35,500 m³ LNG tanker, with a containment system of the Gaz Transport membrane type. The ship was also equipped with reliquefaction equipment to enable her to transport LPG and ethylene.

After delivery from the shipyard at the beginning of 1975, the ship completed successful cargo trials at the LNG terminal of Barcelona, Spain and, as there was no opportunity for a cargo of LNG, she was ordered to load a full cargo of LPG in Arzew, Algeria for Japan. This was the time when the Suez canal was blocked and the most convenient route was therefore through the Panama Canal.

Already, on arrival at Cristobal, there was a call from the Captain, who was being threatened with jail by the port authorities, following the spillage on deck of approximately 50 litres of fuel at the end of bunkering. A guaranty of 1,000 US Dollars was arranged via the agent, which allowed the Captain to return on board and the ship to continue her voyage.

Two days later, there was another radio call, this time explaining the troubles the Chief Engineer was experiencing with the fresh water evaporators.

One evaporator was definitely out of service and the other one was being cleaned. Due to some unexpected purging required, following the malfunction of the evaporators, there was only sufficient fresh or distilled water left on board to proceed for another 12 hours, during which time the second evaporator would be put back into service and hopefully produce more water. However, should the second evaporator also fail, the boilers would have to be stopped. The ship was 200 miles off the coast of Mexico with no nearby traffic and a good weather forecast. It was agreed to resume communication in twelve hours.

The next radio conversation established that there was no fresh or distilled water left on board, the second evaporator was not producing any water and the boilers had been stopped to avoid any serious tube damage due to water starvation. The situation of the ship was reassessed and, again, found to be reasonably safe. There was no traffic to speak of, the weather forecast was good and the vessel was slowly drifting off shore. Tarpaulins had been laid to collect rain water for domestic consumption and the captain and crew were prepared to bide their time in this situation.

The Company Emergency Team was promptly assembled and alternative solutions envisaged. Eventually, it turned out that one LPG ship under charter to our company was just passing through the Panama lakes. That ship was asked to load some fresh water from the lakes, which is suitable for use in boilers, into her ballast tanks to deliver to the drifting ship.

Three days later, the two ships met, transferred the water and the situation returned to normal. The LNG tanker was sent to Acapulco to pick up the service representative for the fresh water evaporators and then sailed to Los Angeles where more serious repairs were arranged before continuing the voyage to Japan where the cargo was eventually safely discharged.

The reason for this incident, which could have led to a much more serious situation, was the engineering crew's lack of familiarity with the type of fresh water evaporator in use on the ship. This was eventually corrected through some intensive training and some crew reshuffling.

12.4.3 AN EXAMPLE OF BRITTLE FRACTURE!

Sometime during the eighties, a ship was discharging LNG in a well known European terminal. For an unknown reason, one liquid valve was not completely closed and when the pumping started, part of the LNG, instead of going ashore as expected, found its way up mast no. 1 and overflowed on to the deck. It took a few minutes for the crew to realise what was happening, by which time the damage was done. The amount of liquid spilled was probably no more than 30 or 40 cubic metres, but the results were spectacular. (See Photos Nos. 91, 92, 93.)

This sort of incident is an ever-present risk for crews operating LNG, and to a lesser extent LPG, ships. Warnings about the risk of brittle fracture are a basic part of their training. However, as the cargo remains mostly within the completely closed piping network, it can be difficult to visualise the kind of damage that a few litres

of liquid can do to normal steel. The following photographs show enough to illustrate the danger of such an incident and the extent of the damage which can result in but a few minutes.

12.4.4 A CALL TO BEIRUT, LEBANON, IN MARCH 1976, TO DISCHARGE A PART−CARGO OF LPG

The very brave superintendent involved in this adventure, a good friend of mine, was sent to Beirut by the company to supervise the discharging operations of a 12,000 m^3 semi-pressurised LPG tanker. He received a hint of things to come when, on arrival at Beirut airport, he found that the only way to board the ship off-shore was by rowing boat.

92. Brittle Fractures caused by Leakage of LNG.
(The Author.)

91. Brittle Fractures caused by Leakage of LNG.
(The Author.)

93. Brittle Fractures caused by Leakage of LNG.
(The Author.)

In Beirut, LPG was normally discharged through sea-lines. There were three sea-lines in use, but at that time there was also a war going on between Christian militias, Palestinians and Islamic activist groups. Beirut port was in flames and it was impossible to anchor near by the first sea-line. The third sea-line at Djouniye, in the Christian area, was under constant fire from heavy guns. The only possibility was the intermediate sea-line between Beirut and Djouniye, which was subjected to only sporadic fire from light guns. The ship was moored across with two anchors and the sea-line connected with the assistance of two local helpers in a rowing boat.

The use of all radio contact was prohibited and communication with the small terminal onshore could only be carried out by flag or light signals.

Discharge started and, at first, all went well. But when it was time to stop, the terminal no longer answered. Night was falling and the ship had already suffered a few hits on the poop deck, in the tank insulation and even one in the pump room bulkhead. It was necessary to go ashore to advise the terminal that discharge was complete, and that the pipe would be disconnected after having been purged under pressure and to obtain an acknowledgement of the quantity discharged.

The superintendent used the two local helpers and their rowing boat to reach the shore, where he had to take cover crawling beside a railway track using the carriages as protection from the shooting in progress. Twice he was stopped by armed militia, though he had no way of knowing to which side they belonged. They took him under armed guard to the terminal where he got the necessary documents signed. They brought him back along the same railtrack, still under armed guard, but this time, walking upright, to the small boat which took him back on board. The ship sailed that night and his final comment was that "no lights were necessary as the bay of Beirut was all aglow and burning"

94. LPG Tanker Involved in the Incident in Beirut. (The Author.)

12.4.5 AN ATTEMPT AT JETTISONING LNG

In most safety manuals written for LPG or LNG tankers, jettisoning cargo is given as the solution to be adopted to lighten the ship in case of a stranded vessel and all ships are equipped with a jettisoning nozzle. This might give the non-informed reader the impression that, in the most desperate situation, there is still something which can be done. However, the way to proceed to jettison a cargo of LPG or LNG is very much unknown. Some reasonably successful trials were carried out by a large oil company on one of a series of LNG ships built in the 1970's. However, those ships were equipped with a stern discharge line, which made the operation quite different from jettisoning to be done on the ship's side from cargo manifolds located amidship.

In December 1981, we had just completed the cargo trials of a newly-delivered 130,000 m³ LNG tanker, with a five tank Gaz Transport membrane type containment system, in Arzew, Algeria. Due to a delay in the start of the project, the ship had to be laid-up for one or two years and had to be gas-freed before being taken to the lay-up site. At the end of the cargo trials, approximately 900 m³ of LNG remained in the tanks and this product had to be vaporised or otherwise disposed of before arrival at Canvey Island where the ship was to receive nitrogen to gas-free the cargo containment system. (The ships of this series are not equipped with inert gas generators and have to rely on an outside supply of nitrogen for gas-freeing.)

On Friday 4th December, the ship was approximately 40 miles North West of Cap Finistere in the Bay of Biscay. There was no traffic within a radius of 20 miles or more and the wind had increased to force 8 (25 to 30 knots).

After consultation with our Head Office, it was decided to proceed with the jettisoning of the remaining cargo, as an experiment to find out if such an operation could really be successfully achieved.

The following precautions were taken:

*95. Preparations Prior to Jettisoning.
(The Author.)*

• All doors and windows of accommodation and machinery rooms were closed and all air conditioning systems put on 100% recirculation.

• A constant flow of water was arranged along most of the port side of the hull with a combination of fire hoses and the permanent water spray system.

- A constant monitoring of gas concentrations was arranged on all deck areas and in the accommodation with fixed and portable gas analysers.

- All senior officers were at their respective posts of responsibility and were in constant communication through portable radios.

The ship was maintaining a course of 350 degrees at a speed of 14 knots and the wind was from the North-East. At 10.30 hours, after installing the jettissoning nozzle, the cargo piping was pressurised with one cargo pump in service and the manifold valve was opened.

As soon as LNG started to flow through the jettison pipe it was obvious that vapour from the vaporised liquid was coming back alongside the ship instead of being dispersed away, and the operation was stopped.

Due to the ship's high superstructures, an area of low pressure was created towards the aft part of the hull on the side opposite to the wind and the LNG vapour was attracted to this area.

96. The First Attempt. (The Author.)

159

97. The First Attempt. (The Author.)

98. The First Attempt. (The Author.)

It was not possible to jettison cargo safely in these conditions.

After a debriefing, it was decided to have another try in the afternoon, with the ship in a different position in relation to the wind.

The operation was repeated at 14.00 hours, with the ship sailing a course of 260 to 280 degrees at 3 to 4 knots, with the wind, still 25 knots, coming from aft or three-quarter starboard side. After a few minutes of pumping LNG out in these conditions, the vapour cloud was again starting to come alongside the ship and the operation was stopped once again.

The next try was made with the ship in the same position but stopped or going astern at 1 knot. The original idea was for the ship to steam astern, but it was not possible to steer the ship with enough accuracy to guarantee a stable position relative to the wind.

In this way, it was found to be possible to pump the LNG out with the vapour cloud following the wind forward of the ship. The end of the jettison pipe was 17 metres above the water. When pumping with one pump at an estimated flow of 1,200 m^3/hour, the liquid flow was almost totally vaporised before touching the water.

99. The Second Attempt with One Pump in Service. (The Author.)

161

100. The Second Attempt with One Pump in Service. (The Author.)

101. The Second Attempt with Two Pumps in Service. (The Author.)

102. The Second Attempt with Two Pumps in Service. (The Author.)

A second pump was started and the flow increased to about 2,000 m³/hour. Then the liquid LNG was seen touching the water and some very strong explosion noises were noticed. The second pump was stopped. The operation was continued until 16.00 hours. An estimated 700 m³ of LNG had been jettisoned and the quantity remaining on board could only be pumped out with the stripping pumps.

During the whole pumping operation, the flow of liquid was maintained at approximately 10 metres away from the hull and the white cloud of vapour was flowing towards the forward part of the ship, barely touching the port-side deck. The gas analysers were showing 50% of LEL at the fringe of the cloud.

The operation had finally been possible but the main engine and the steering had to be used constantly to maintain the wind coming from aft of the ship and to maintain the flow of liquid as far as possible from the hull. It would probably be quite difficult to continue pumping in these conditions during the time it would take to empty a whole cargo, particularly if the wind was not as strong as it was that day. For a stranded ship, the chances of being able to jettison cargo safely without being able to control her position relative to the wind would be very slim.

Fortunately, the safety record of liquefied gas tankers is extremely good and we have seen that, even with very serious damage to the hull, the cargo containment remains intact.

The explosions which were heard when the flow of LNG was increased were probably due to the phenomenon of Rapid Phase Transition (RPT) which occurs when "old" LNG enters into contact with water. The LNG pumped out during this experiment had been transferred from tank to tank during cargo trials and had probably lost a certain amount of its lighter components. It could be qualified as "old".

Enough stories for now. It would not be difficult to keep going though! There is never a dull moment when operating liquefied gas tankers. This is what makes it so interesting. I did it for twenty-five years and would be ready for another twenty-five!

103. The Ship's Funnel. (The Author.)

CONCLUSION

Any reader having reached this point in the book should have a good understanding of the development of the marine transportation of liquefied gases through the years, of its present situation, its organisation and the problems it is facing.

The future of the industry appears good today. The LPG and chemical gases trades continue to progress slowly but steadily and great expectations are placed on LNG.

The technical development of LPG ships and terminals seemed to have reached a plateau some twenty-five years ago. But new equipment is constantly being introduced, which moves the technology. The more recent developments affect the control and measurement equipment, the refrigeration plants and the production of inert gas, to list only the more visible improvements.

The design and construction of LNG liquefaction and storage plants have seen considerable developments in recent years, aimed mainly at greater efficiency and a reduction of production price. The design of LNG ships could give the impression not to have changed much in twenty years. However, the construction technology has substantially evolved, allowing ships of similar design and size to be built for a lesser amount of US Dollars today than twenty years ago.

Substantial changes in the technical design of LNG ships are ready for implementation but are still waiting for an order. Different types of propulsion systems, boil-off reliquefaction units and increases in ship size are the more obvious.

It is probable that, with the constant pressure to reduce the transport cost for new contracts, one or more of these changes will eventually be adopted in the near future.

The strong demand for a reduction in the delivery price of LNG is a trend which requires careful watching. It is certainly legitimate to improve the technical and commercial efficiency of a system. The danger is that cost cutting measures may be applied inappropriately, as was done in the rest of the shipping industry, which could reduce the outstanding safety level, which is one of the great successes of the marine transportation of liquefied gases. Liquefied gas production units, storage plants and ships are high-cost equipment and, in order to maximise the return on investment, they are expected to serve for many years. To achieve this, they need to be constructed according to very good technical designs and with first-class materials, to ensure good reliability throughout their life. Likewise, the ships need to be manned by a sufficient complement of well-qualified officers and crew, able not only to operate but also to maintain them in good condition. They also need to be regularly serviced and upgraded through the years.

This requires continuous and consistent efforts from all parties involved. The success of LNG so far has been due to its clean image, also its reliable and safe availability. To have a cheaper product with an inconsistent delivery schedule and a risky safety level would certainly not improve its image and its competitiveness.

INDEX

169

104. Issue of Stamps for the Opening of the Yung-An LNG Terminal, Kaohsiung, Taiwan (31 March, 1990).